Bellevue
Literary
Review

*A journal of humanity
and human experience*

Volume 9, Number 2, Fall 2009
Department of Medicine
NYU Langone Medical Center
www.BLReview.org

The *Bellevue Literary Review* is published twice a year by the Department of Medicine at NYU Langone Medical Center.

Subscriptions available at www.BLReview.org (1 year: $15 ♦ 3 years: $35)

The Editors invite submissions of previously unpublished works of fiction, nonfiction, and poetry that touch upon relationships to the human body, illness, health, and healing. We encourage creative interpretation of these themes. Manuscripts can be submitted at www.BLReview.org.

Printed by The Sheridan Press Hanover, Pennsylvania
Distributed by Ingram Periodicals and Ubiquity Distributors, Inc.
ISSN 1537-5048   ISBN-13: 978-0-9814891-3-1   ISBN-10: 0-9814891-3-3
Indexed by Humanities International Complete
Member of the Council of Literary Magazines and Presses (CLMP)

The Editorial Staff of the *Bellevue Literary Review* express their deep appreciation to the following people who have assisted with manuscript review: Sarah Bain, David Baldwin, Zachary Berger, Denitza Blagev, Michael Bloom, Andrew Bomback, Michael Brabeck, Rose Bromberg, Caitlin Cox, Sayantani Dasgupta, Rebecca Dillingham, Josh Dolezal, Kathleen Dunn, Marylu Ekiert, Leora Feinblum, Serena Fox, Barbara Galletly, Bracha Goykadosh, Andrea Hines, Susanna Horng, Ed Janowitz, Alison Jarvis, Judy Katz, Jackie Keer, Timothy Kelly, Diana Kole, April Krassner, Charles Langs, Steven Malcic, Susan Malus, Lissa McKinley, Michelle McMacken, Ruth Meehan, Sheila Moaleman, Jacqueline Mosher, Esther Naamat, Ivan Oransky, Ruth Oratz, Barbara Porter, Joseph Rabatin, M.A. Rocks, Shetal Shah, Mary Sharkey, Jamie Smith, Bara Swain, Leah Traube, Benj Vardigan, Laura Willwerth.

We are grateful for the help of Lorinda Klein, and for the continued support of Bellevue Hospital.

Cover Note:

Southfield Ferry, circa 1910

The Southfield Ferry was a retired Staten Island Ferry purchased by the Bellevue Auxiliary in 1908 to serve as a floating sanatorium. It was moored in the East River at E. 26th Street and served as a day treatment facility for tuberculosis patients. Inhaling fresh air—no matter what the weather—was considered the best treatment for TB, and indeed was the only treatment available until the antibiotic isoniazid became available in the early 1950s. Dr. Walsh McDermott, a Bellevue physician, was quoted as saying that the best cure for TB was "to stand on a windy corner." The Southfield Ferry treated patients in two shifts: female patients during the day, male patients—who presumably had jobs—during the night. Rules on the boat were very strict and patients were required to lie completely still during their al fresco treatment.

The Southfield Ferry served Bellevue Hospital until it exploded in 1918 from a boiler accident. It was replaced by the Day-Camp Boat (a retired barge) until 1938 when the FDR Drive was built along the waterfront as part of a massive WPA project. Bellevue had just built its own TB building (the "C&D" building), so the boats were no longer needed.

Photo courtesy of Bellevue Hospital Center Archives

Bellevue Literary Review

A journal of humanity and human experience

Danielle Ofri — *Editor-in-Chief*
Ronna Wineberg — *Senior Fiction Editor*
Jerome Lowenstein — *Senior Nonfiction Editor*
Suzanne McConnell — *Fiction Editor*
Corie Feiner — *Poetry Editor*

Martin J. Blaser — *Publisher*
Stacy Bodziak — *Managing Editor*

Editorial Board

Felice Aull	Will Grossman	Claudia S. Plottel
Carol Berman	Perri E. Klass	Norman A. Posner
Rafael Campo	Itzhak Kronzon	Richard Selzer
Rita Charon	George Lipkin	Marc Siegel
Jack Coulehan	Lois Lowenstein	Abraham Verghese
Tony Dajer	Sherwin Nuland	Gerald Weissmann
Stuart Dickerman	David Oshinsky	David Zimmerman
Kate Falvey	Michael Pillinger	Abigail Zuger

Troi Santos — *Graphic Designer*
Lucy Cribben — *Department Administrator*
Elsa Nunez — *Office Associate*
Renata Broderick, — *Interns*
Alexandra Ozols,
Caran Wakefield

Contents

Volume 9, Number 2, Fall 2009

Fiction

Nonfiction

Poetry

Foreword

"You opened this door…"

So begins Melissa Stein's poem, "Hinges," appearing in this issue of the *Bellevue Literary Review*. It is an apt description for much of the writing we receive. Our themes seem to inspire writers to dig a bit deeper, to enter the realms that are slivered open when illness invades. The ways in which we are broken and healed press these doors even further ajar, allowing us to consider the fragility of the human experience.

When asked to describe our themes, we often say that we are looking for writing on "illness, health, and healing." However, this is a deceptively simple phrase. Yes, on the surface these are stories, essays, and poems about disease and healing, about the mind and body. But they are more than that. They take the reader into intimate spaces and help us find that common place—that *human* place—where we can slip into another person's experience.

Several pieces in this issue are meditations on loss. In "A Distant Shore," by Patrick Pfister, our narrator—on the cusp of moving from hospital to hospice—is charged with taking stock of his life in order to find some kind of peace before death. MaryLee McNeal's "Smart Enough" approaches loss from a different angle, as a man who has spent his life under the thumb of his domineering mother is suddenly 'free' after her death. Nancy Naomi Carlson's "What Bears Your Name" is a beautiful poem about honoring a child's "one day of life."

Other pieces in this issue also consider birth and childhood. Christopher Schacht's "Shark Eyes" turns an unflinching eye to what constitutes living when twins are delivered prematurely. In "Martin, 1918," Karina Borowicz describes a childhood cut short by "the epidemic standing sentinel/ at the border between twelve and thirteen." The young narrator in Kelly Flanigan's "To the River" also sees his childhood contract when he must cope with tragedy in his friend's family and uncertainty in his own. In "Before the Jacaranda Trees Bloom," by Sequoia Nagamatsu, two recent college graduates spend a summer at a hospice in South Africa, mourning the end of their relationship while helping a young boy grieve the impending loss of his mother to AIDS.

All of the essays in this volume contemplate family relationships: what we inherit, what is lost, and how lives are interwoven despite the fractures of time and place. P. Philip Cheung's "My Father's Hands" focuses on the intangibles that his father has passed on to him, delicate talents that were not taught so much as absorbed. Itzhak Kronzon and Kurt Magsamen also pay tribute to fathers—in very different ways—in their essays. Hazel Kight Witham's "The Storm Between Us" parallels the author's struggle with mental illness with that of her grandmother, tracing her birthright back to the hospital where her grandmother endured treatment of a different sort in another era. And in "She Might Die," Magda Montiel Davis reaches back to a time when her mother's future was uncertain and her own capacity to understand was bound by the limitations of childhood.

Other pieces invite us to go along for the ride with their unique characters. In "The Hand You're Dealt," Jerry M. Burger takes us on a journey with a bipolar man searching for connection while in the throes of a manic gambling trip. Luther Magnussen's "At War With General Franco" follows a gallivanting soldier in the Spanish Civil War, weaving his story back and forth through time. And in "This, of Course, Is Spiritual," by Matt Lombardi, we spend time with a writing professor who has locked himself in the school bathroom, where he alternates between raving wildly and calmly teaching class to the students gathered outside the door.

We hope you enjoy 'opening this door' with us. Simply putting together an issue means nothing if it does not reach the hands of passionate readers. We are grateful to everyone who joins our community of subscribers, and to everyone who chooses a copy from the overflowing bookstore racks. We hope that the words in the *BLR* stimulate discussion and reflection, and that you'll be inspired—to share the journal and to share your own stories.

Stacy Bodziak
Managing Editor

The Hand You're Dealt

Jerry M. Burger

I say I'll keep taking the lithium, but the doubt I see on Dr. Pederson's face as he hands me the pills tells me I probably won't. And then it's time to go. Only the real nutcases stay at the VA more than a couple of days anymore. Better for you on the outside, they say. Institutionalization can be worse than the disease. But we all know it's the budget cuts. They don't have half the staff they did the first time I was here. I'm released after breakfast. Pederson insists that all psychiatric patients wear their own clothes, so there's not even anything to change into before I find myself standing at the bus stop in front of the hospital. I've got a brown paper bag in my right hand that contains some toiletries. In my left, a 30-day supply of the miracle drug that lowers the highs and raises the lows. Good old lithium. Safest medication we hand out, Pederson says. Consider yourself lucky to be bipolar. Look at the facial tics and memory loss the schizos have to put up with.

I hope to sneak into Mom's house unnoticed, but she's got the doors locked and has once again moved the hidden key. I knock, and when she sees me through the opening in the chained doorway she can't hold back the forlorn "Oh" that escapes her lips.

"They released you," she says.

"I've got medication."

"Lithium again?"

I pull the plastic bottle from my jacket pocket and let her read the label. A scowl crosses her face as she releases the chain. "The clothes you left are in the guest room."

On the bed I find a pair of running shoes covered with mud, and the five pairs of plaid pants I bought in one doozy of a manic episode. The pants still bear the store tags. Fifty percent off. No wonder I couldn't resist. Mom makes no mention of me staying a few days, and the way she has laid out the pants and shoes suggests they're to be picked up and taken with me. I wore out my welcome years ago.

"You still got the apartment?" Mom is standing in the bedroom doorway. Hints of maternal concern creep into her voice.

"At least until the end of the month." I roll the pants up and tuck them under my arm. "But I could use some money."

She nods. "Lose your job at the frame store?"

"Probably. I haven't been there in a week."

She steps to another room and returns with five twenty-dollar bills. The usual amount. Neither of us could begin to guess how much money she's given me since my discharge from the Marines two days after my 22nd birthday. I turn 27 next month.

She presses the money into my palm. "No gambling, OK?"

"No gambling."

Nine days later I'm on the Greyhound from San Francisco to Reno. I haven't slept in thirty-six hours—one of Pederson's seven warning signs. At the VA, the bipolars keep notebooks next to their beds. We mark off hours of sleep with red X's. Fewer than five X's in a 24-hour period and they up your meds. It's their answer to all of life's problems. Take a pill. Take a pill. Take a pill. So I take their pill. And then I stop.

It's 6:26 in the morning, and there are only twelve people on the whole damned bus, counting me but not the driver. No one's talking, not even the people sitting together. All I can hear are the shivers of road noise that run through the bus. I change seats, searching for company. No one will look me in the eye.

What's the matter with you? It's Pederson's voice. *Why did you stop taking your medicine?* It's a stupid question. Because something is better than nothing. Because you can burn up in the flame, but you can also die in the dark. One way or the other, I've got to find out where this magic carpet is taking me and, in the end, whether the ride is worth the price of the ticket.

I move to the seat behind the driver. He is a large black man. Rolls of fat tucked into his tight-fitting shirt hang over his leather belt. A sign clipped to the sun visor says his name is Monroe.

"I'm Winston," I say. "I'm planning to win a fortune at Harrah's. What do you think?"

Monroe grunts. "Heard that before."

"Not a gambling man?" I ask. "Hell, life's a gamble. Win or lose. You got to choose." I tap out a rhythm on the metal bar that separates us.

"You know about Huntington's disease?" I ask. "They used to call it Huntington's chorea. Terrible disease. Waits until you're forty, then turns your brain into jello. And here's the hell of it. If one of your parents has Huntington's, you got a fifty-fifty chance of getting it yourself. Imagine that? Your old man has the disease, only he doesn't find out until you're like twenty years old yourself. That's when they break the news to you—it's even odds that you'll end up with a mush brain yourself someday. Fifty-fifty. Even Steven. You think Harrah's gives even odds on anything?"

Monroe tilts his head to look at me in the rear-view mirror but doesn't say anything.

"But save your tears, Monroe," I say. "This story has a happy ending. Because now they can tell if you got the genetic marker. And not just for Huntington's. They can do a test on you to see if you got tagged for Alzheimer's or diabetes or schizophrenia. You name it. Now how's that for fair? Your parents get to roll the dice for you. They squeak the springs one night, and out of all the millions of little sperm cells the one with the Huntington's marker or the hearing-things marker or maybe the want-to-kill-yourself marker hits the jackpot. And before you ever see the light of day, your hand's already been dealt. And all you can do is play what they gave you or fold. Now what kind of goddamned choice is that?"

Monroe grunts again and adjusts his cap. "The company discourages us from talking with passengers."

I get the message. I bounce from seat to seat, desperately searching for one that fits my spine. Half the people on the bus are sleeping. The hum of the engine falls into a pattern. Da Da *Bump*. Da Da *Bump*. It's like someone's thumping the top of the roof. I put my fingers in my ears, but the vibration travels through me. Da Da *Bump*. It's impossible to concentrate on anything else. But somehow these mannequins all around me manage to sleep through it.

I count the trees. I count red cars. I count the miles to Reno, but somebody has been messing with the road signs. It takes hours to travel between the 76- and the 72-mile marker. Just when I think I'm going to scream, I see the Greyhound sign up ahead. I race to the front of the bus. Monroe tells me to return to my seat. I walk halfway to the rear, pivot, then race back to the front just as we pull into the station.

The door opens, and suddenly I'm on the outside. Free of the bus and free of those goddamned lifeless zombies. Monroe yells at me. Did I bring any luggage?

"No," I yell back. At least I don't think so.

I'm almost running by the time I get to Harrah's. I push through the glass door and suddenly I'm caught in a storm of flashing lights and noise. Jackpot bells are singing, coins are clanging, lights are beckoning. Red, gold, white, green, red, gold, red. I absorb the energy in the room through my skin. People are moving. Sliding and weaving like a cavern full of serpents. The smell of money and hope and cigarette smoke burns my nostrils. This is where I belong. The smile on my face is so wide my cheeks hurt.

How do you feel? Pederson again. How do you feel? How do you feel? It's his mantra. Every time you see him on the ward. Every group meeting. We go around the circle and everyone answers the question. How do you feel? But Pederson's never been where I'm at right now, so he'll never get it. When you're way up or way down, you don't *feel*. You just *are*. That's the problem with their precious lithium. They fill you up with chemicals, and then you're someone's creation. The end product of the ingredients they put inside you. A character in someone else's play. Who would you like me to be, Dr. Pederson? A productive member of society? A decorated member of the United States Marines? A problem-free son a mother can be proud of? Mix up the recipe and let me have it. How do I feel? However you want me to.

I head for the blackjack tables, but I don't know if I can sit still long enough to play. If I'm not mistaken, that's another warning sign. There's an intensity coming from the cards and the chips that draws me in. I see a table with five people. There's an empty chair, but I don't like to play with crowds. Too many people to wait on while they make up their goddamned minds and play their goddamned hands. I find another table that has only two players, but the dealer is wearing blue earrings, and I know that'll be unlucky.

Third try is the charm. The dealer has bright red fingernails and earrings to match. Red, like diamonds and hearts. Red, like the heart of a fire. There's only two people at the table *and* one of them is a redhead. I take a seat. This is where I was meant to be.

I buy fifty dollars worth of chips, then stack and restack them into piles of fives, then tens, then fives, then tens while I wait for the cards to come. The redhead sitting next to me is just about the skinniest woman I've ever seen. She's got like eight copper bracelets on her bony right arm that sound like a slinky going up and down every time she lifts her glass of booze to her face.

My first card is a red queen. Of course it is. I want to thank the redhead for what she's done for me. I want to kiss her on her skinny lips and buy her another drink. The dealer hits on a thirteen and busts. I win three hands in a row, lose one when I stay on fifteen, then run off four more winners. I look around, hoping to see Monroe the bus driver. Luck, I want to scream at him. When you see it, catch it. Then ride it for as long and as far as it will take you. It's the ride you live for, Monroe. Without the promise of exhilaration, the moments in between would be intolerable.

A blond waitress in a black velvet outfit asks if I want something to drink. Her push-up bra is smashing her little boobs together in a desperate attempt to create some cleavage. I drop a five-dollar tip on her tray and tell her my name.

"Nothing for me just yet, hon," I say. "But maybe if you come back a little later."

The redhead next to me orders a drink. It's not yet two in the afternoon and she wants another straight shot of Johnny Walker Red. Johnny Walker *Red.* Need a better omen than that? I double my bet on the next hand and win again. I'm sitting behind a castle of chips, more than a dozen stacks all exactly the same height. An oasis of red, white, and blue in a sea of green felt.

"Keep 'em coming," I say to the red-earringed dealer. I slide another stack of chips next to my bet.

"Not going to save any of that for a rainy day?" she asks. "Maybe quit while you're ahead?"

"The moment you quit," I tell her, "you're no longer ahead."

Then the skinny redhead downs the last of her Johnny Walker Red and leaves the table. The dealer tosses me a seven, then an eight. Both black. She gives herself two tens. Shit. I double my usual bet and go bust. Sitting on twelve and she throws me a king. Next hand starts with a five and a jack. Things are starting to spiral. Why isn't *that* on Pederson's list? Warning sign number eight—the ground beneath you gives way and you find yourself sucked into a vacuum beneath your feet.

I wipe my upper lip and leave a line of perspiration on my sleeve. It's hotter than hell in here and someone has turned up the noise on the slot machines. Coins crash violently into metal trays. Alarms roar overhead. I can't buy a face card. The whole damned deck is made up of clubs and spades, and not one of them is higher than an eight. My mouth is dry and I can't find the blond waitress in the push-up bra.

I reach for another stack of chips and find that my fortress is gone. I turn to the dealer for an explanation, but the woman with the red fingernails and earrings to match is also gone. In her place I find a dark-skinned girl with high cheekbones and no jewelry. The other players at the table also have changed since I last took inventory of the situation. A row of quarter slots that were not operating when I first sat down are now chirping and chiming to my left.

"Would you like to buy some chips?" the new dealer asks.

"No, I would not like to buy some chips," I tell her. "I would like the chips I've already won returned to me immediately."

There's a man looking over my right shoulder. As I sense his presence, I'm aware that he has been standing in this same location for some time. He has large pockets on his coat, a perfect place to hide the stacks of chips he has somehow managed to slip away from me while I was concentrating on my cards. I spin in his direction.

"I'll take my chips back now, if you don't mind."

He looks at me with guilt written all over his face, then tries to slip away with my winnings still in his pocket. I have only a split second to act. I dive toward him, my right hand reaching into his coat pocket, my left arm wrapping around his legs. We tumble into a crowd of people. There's screaming and people falling, and my face is pressed into the carpet. I manage to throw off the bodies and rise to my feet. But the thief is gone.

I see a large security guard in a black coat striding in my direction. He's got protruding lips and waddles when he steps, which makes me think of Daffy Duck. Daffy stops several feet in front of me, his feet spread shoulder width. He tells me it's time to leave.

"I'll leave when I get my money back."

"You'll leave now, or I'll escort you out."

I size him up. Daffy is big, but vulnerable. No flexibility. No agility. By the time he lifts his arms, I could land a dozen punches. I glance around. He might have friends in the crowd. He takes another step my way. I have to land the first punch.

But someone tips him off. Daffy moves before I'm ready. My arm is behind my back and it feels like he's pulling it out of the socket. He pushes me through the gathered crowd, which parts like the Red Sea. We're moving much too fast. We sail through the open doorway like two speed-skaters. I can't tell when Daffy lets go, but as I trip over some blue-haired geezer, he's no longer there to support me. I topple forward, my forehead bouncing off the concrete. I press my face against the cold pavement. My body temperature seems to be dangerously high.

The next thing I know, I'm walking the streets of Reno, Nevada, watching each step instead of the people who keep running into me as I try to move forward. I'm aware of very little except that the situation has darkened. Peering up through the artificial light, I see the sky also is dark. A great deal of time has passed.

Somewhere between sitting down at the blackjack table and being escorted out of the casino, I've lost my jacket. If that's not one of Pederson's warning signs, it ought to be.

I lean against a light post. I don't have enough energy to keep moving. I recognize the symptoms, but this is not the way it works. I've never come down from a high so fast. Maybe I hit my head too hard. Maybe I'm bleeding inside my skull. I think I can feel the blood oozing over my brain cells, coating my defective genes.

I look around and see the gray shapes of people passing by. I don't recognize the place, but strangely it has the feel of a memory. Mostly I want to sleep. A police car drives by slowly, the officer on the passenger side looks at me through the open window. An instinct tells me to move on.

I push my way through the first casino door I find. The flashing lights hurt my eyes. I have a headache that runs above my eyebrows and down to the back of my neck. I'm certain my brain is bleeding.

There's a bar in the corner that is darker than the rest of the room. I take my place on an empty stool. A mirror behind the bartender spans the entire length of the bar, reminding drinkers that there's a casino full of gambling options just behind them. When I stare straight ahead, I see myself. My eyes are red, and my cheeks are round and puffy. One side of my face is larger than the other. I think I just might be the least attractive person I have ever seen.

I dig into my pockets and lay everything in my possession on the counter. Twelve dollars and fifty-five cents, plus the key to my apartment and a thin, empty wallet.

The woman sitting next to me reaches for her drink and clangs her metal bracelets against the edge of the bar. It's the redhead from the blackjack table.

"Johnny Walker Red," I say.

We meet eyes by looking at each other in the mirror. She lifts her glass in salute. "Pretty good guess."

She finishes her drink while I scan the bottles along the back of the bar, trying to remember what I drink to complement a black mood. I feel an obligation to do this thing right.

The redhead catches the bartender's eye and points to her empty glass. "Another."

I point to the space in front of me. "I'll have the same."

I don't recall if I've ever had straight shots of whiskey before, and the sensation as the liquor hits my lips and tongue is startling. It feels like I've placed a burning match in my mouth. But I let the liquid scorch a trail all the way down my throat. Somehow the pain belongs in the scene.

No words pass between us for several minutes, but the redhead and I are aware of each other. We respond to the other person's movements with our own twitches and leans, and are careful to lower the liquor in our glasses at the same pace. We are drinking alone together.

"I'm Winston," I say, staring into the top of my glass.

"Ronnie." She sips her drink. "Short for Veronica."

She turns toward me, and it seems to me we recognize something in each other. It happens all the time on the ward. You lock eyes with a depressed patient and see a reflection of what you feel inside. Ronnie's eyes are amber and surprisingly clear for a woman who has been drinking as much as I think she has. If not for the bags under her eyes, I'd wonder if she were old enough to sit at a bar.

She nods toward the crumpled bills and loose change in front of me. "That all you got in the world?"

"Just about."

"Then I'd say you're *just about* at the end of your rope."

The truth in her statement is so obvious that there is no need to respond.

"You believe in luck?" Ronnie asks.

"I don't appear to have any, if that's what you mean."

"I can see *that*," she says. "But do you think there's some people who are born lucky?"

I look at my reflection in the mirror. "I know for a fact some people are born unlucky."

"I think some people shit and it turns to gold," she says. "And the rest of us—if we ever get our hands on a lump of gold, it turns to shit."

"So what can you do about it?"

"Something," she says. "Maybe."

We finish our drinks and Ronnie asks if she can buy me another. The second shot burns less than the first. I'm still spiraling, but the booze or some other change in my neurological chemistry has put my descent in a holding pattern. Time is passing, but I experience it only as a series of jumps from one moment to the next. At some point Ronnie waves yet again to the bartender, but when he takes away our empty glasses he says, "Maybe you two should take it easy for a while. I can order some food if you want."

A meal seems like a good idea. I can't recall the last time I ate. But Ronnie pushes herself away from the bar so violently she knocks her stool to the ground.

"Fuck that," she yells. "You think I came here for the fine cuisine?"

She grabs her purse off the counter, gives the bartender the finger and leaves. I stare into the mirror. There's a desperate sense of emptiness in the room now that slowly overtakes me. I turn to follow Ronnie.

I find her just outside the door, where she's lighting a cigarette and swearing to no one about the bartender. She nods in my direction, and we start walking.

"You taking meds?" she asks.

"Not at the moment."

"I've done them all. Prozac, Zoloft." She sounds as if she's barking out a cadence. "Paxil, Elavil, Amitril. They've inhibited my MAOs and tinkered with my seratonin uptake. And now they're talking about electroshock. Fucking zap your brain cells with electricity. Knock that depression right out of your skull. You ever try that?"

"I'm bipolar," I say. "They only do that electricity stuff with the straight depressives."

We are in an alleyway between two large buildings. Even in the dim light I see tears have appeared on Ronnie's face. I've been there before. Too depressed to recognize when the tears are on or off. No noticeable difference between crying and not crying.

"You ever going back?" Ronnie asks. "Back to the doctors and the pills and the crazies?"

"I always do."

"What for?" Ronnie tosses her half-smoked cigarette to the ground and crushes it with the heel of her boot. "Tell me why you keep going back."

I have no immediate answer. Because that's what I do, I say to myself.

"We don't have to put up with it, you know," Ronnie says. "Just because we got a shitty deal out of life, there's nothing that says we have to be miserable for eighty years."

Ronnie stops walking. She looks around to make sure we are alone in the alley. Then she sticks her hand into her purse and pulls out a gun.

"We can put an end to it any time we decide." Ronnie holds the gun at eye level for my inspection. It's a short-barrel revolver with a dull gray finish.

"I tried once before, you know." She pulls her bracelets up to her elbow and holds her right wrist a few inches from my face. I see the scars. Three white lines overlapping the blue veins protruding from her skinny arm. "My mistake was using the wrong method."

"Is that what you came here to do?" I ask.

"You be my witness," she says. "You're better than a note. You know what it's like. They'll ask you why, and you'll ask them to give a reason why not."

I hear Pederson's voice screaming from somewhere behind my ears. *She's not thinking clearly. Things are never as bad as they seem. There's always hope.* But I refuse to listen. Ronnie doesn't need that bullshit right now. She needs a reason why not. Just one damned reason. But I don't know exactly what that is, because I've almost—*almost*—been there myself. At that moment when not being makes as much sense as being. When relief is so close you can start to feel it. Maybe it's a false moment, a false promise. But who the hell am I to tell Ronnie or anyone else what's real and what's not?

Ronnie wraps both hands around the gun as if embracing a treasure. She lifts the revolver to eye level. I wonder if she was at least allowed a happy childhood, maybe even a high school boyfriend and a senior prom. Maybe she was given at least that much. Our eyes meet and I can see the decision has been made. Maybe it was made a long time ago, when her chromosomes locked in place and wrote the script. Maybe she's just been waiting for the ending all this time.

I'm so afraid, my hands are shaking.

Ronnie holds the gun in front of her eyes for a moment, as if considering one last time the specifics of how she wants to do it. Then she lowers the gun to her lips and points it upward toward the roof of her mouth. I can imagine the bullet, released from its chamber and sent flying through the barrel, up through the middle of her brain. I can see it in slow motion, ripping through vital centers until it explodes out the other end of her skull. And I wonder if, during that split second when the bullet is on its way, if she'll have the slightest doubt, a too-late change of heart.

Then a hand comes from somewhere and slaps the revolver away. The gun spins through the air and lands with a crack, then skids along the asphalt. We are both silent for a moment, breathing rapidly and trying to understand what just happened. I stare into her face and then at my outstretched arm. The hand belongs to me.

We grab one another and slowly drop to the cold asphalt. We are both exhausted. Her eyes ask, *why*? I have nothing to tell her. It was as much an act of survival as a rescue.

An unknowable amount of time passes, and I feel Ronnie shaking in my arms.

"Where's home?" I ask. My voice is barely audible.

"Riverside."

"Got money for a bus ride?"

She buries her face in my shoulder and nods.

I stand and help Ronnie to her feet. We move toward the glow of the lights, but she stops to look in the direction of the gun. Its outline is barely visible against the dark asphalt. A moment passes, then she takes my arm and we turn together in the opposite direction.

The bus station is but four blocks away. It seems to me like it should be farther. ✀

July, 1979

Flavian Mark Lupinetti

"I'll close," I say to my resident. Usually she moves with the precision and grace of a ballerina, but my offer takes her by surprise and she makes a spastic little jerk, dropping her instruments. She backs away from the table quickly, tearing off her gloves, as if I might change my mind if she doesn't break scrub fast enough.

"Thanks," she says, her voice betraying a small sigh of relief. "I gotta get some good clothes on. For the thing." I nod. The thing.

"Hey." I stop her before she gets out the door. I jerk my head toward the medical students, standing at the foot of the table with their hands clasped in front of them like pensive squirrels. "Take them with you. They want a big crowd." For the thing.

They troop out, leaving only Lorraine, my scrub nurse, to help me close the patient. She is surprised as well to see me assume this menial task. "Still remember how?" When she says this, her eyes—the only portion of her face visible above her mask—crinkle in a smile.

"Help me if I forget something."

I find it oddly gratifying, this simple, repetitive sewing of muscle and fascia, a relief from the meticulous reconstruction of tiny blood vessels I've spent the last four hours on, but Lorraine's dig is warranted. It's been years since I've closed. After putting in the last stitch I sit in the corner and do the paperwork—brief op note, orders—and I grab the face sheet for the billing.

An orderly sticks his head into the room. He sees that the patient is closed and that Lorraine is breaking down her instruments, so he drops his mask. "Dr. Hansen called. Wondered where you were."

Hansen, the new chief of surgery. Five years now, and they still call him the new chief. I do too. "Jesus. It's not for ten minutes. Tell him I'll be there."

I go to the locker room, strip off my scrubs, and don my street clothes. White coat or sport jacket? I choose the former. Then I hop down the back stairs to avoid as many people as possible, and I emerge from the utility stairwell into the hall outside the auditorium. Here I can no longer avoid the crowd, mostly dressed in black. For many, this is the first time they have seen each other in years, and subdued greetings are mixed with occasional enthusiastic ones that belie the otherwise somber setting.

The wall in the lobby is adorned with the black-trimmed portrait of Richard Jernigan, the former chief of surgery. Or The Chief, as he is still known. I knew him, of course, before he was The Chief. When I first met him, he was younger than I am now.

I do my best to stay on the periphery, but that doesn't spare me from receiving expressions of sympathy. I also do my best to appear appreciative; we did work together for twenty-five years, after all.

There is no explicit announcement, only a lull in the conversations and a nervous cough or two that serve as a signal for us to file into the auditorium. Already in place is the family, sitting in the front row. Hansen is talking to them. About what I can't even imagine. Maybe it is his difficulty in maintaining a conversation that makes him call me by name when I try to slip into a seat at the back of the room, high up with the medical students.

Hansen signals me to occupy the second row, and, when he does, Mrs. Jernigan turns her head and sees me. I descend to floor level and stand before Mrs. Jernigan. Her gray hair is coiffed into tight curls, and she smiles warmly at me. I take her thin, cool hand with its translucent skin and prominent veins.

"So sorry for your loss," I tell her. I try to maintain the right duration of eye contact. Long enough, but not too long.

Don't get injured in July. That's what everyone says. July is when the new interns arrive, and everyone knows you can't trust the new interns. You don't know who's good and who's bad, who's reliable and who's crazy. You have to be wary. If you got injured in July, 1979, the person you had to be wary of was me.

I started my internship on the trauma service. That's the rotation that creates the highest demands on surgery residents, but in some ways it generates the lowest pressure. The demands came from gunshot wounds, knife injuries, and motor vehicle accidents; from shovels, golf clubs, ice axes, baseball bats—wooden and aluminum—guitar strings, liquor bottles, extension cords, and frozen turkeys, all of which had been employed on one occasion or another to assault a person who landed in our ER.

The lower pressure came from our not being responsible. The trauma team doesn't *decide* to operate the way surgeons do for elective cases. You couldn't blame us for the circumstances, so you couldn't blame us for any complications or damages. You couldn't blame us for any deaths. Trauma is low pressure because we weren't the ones who hurt 'em.

I had been on the trauma service for two weeks with no serious screw-ups and was starting to get the hang of the job. It was almost ten o'clock one Thursday night when I got a call from the ER about a hand injury. The textbooks call this thing a boxer's fracture, but it's an injury no real boxer would suffer. When you break the fourth metacarpal, the bone in the hand supporting the ring finger, it means you don't know how to punch. It means, my attendings said, that you punch like a girl. When you punch like a man, it's the knuckles of the first and middle fingers that strike flesh. That's the kind of punch that does damage. A blow struck properly is backed by the sturdy radius and ulna of the forearm, maximizing the impact on your target and protecting the hand from a fracture. But if you punch with the side of the fist, with the knuckles of the ring and little fingers making contact—if you punch like a girl—there's nothing to support the hand's delicate skeleton. The bones break if you hit hard enough.

As soon as I walked into the ER I could tell the patient had a boxer's fracture, even without an X-ray. The swollen left hand, the purple stain with orange at the edge like an Arizona sunset, and the scuff marks just below the wedding ring—I knew it. I may have been a lowly intern, but I'd seen an assload of those things in medical school, and I knew the drill: X-ray to confirm, a gutter-shaped cast running from the little finger to the elbow, six weeks to heal. But they heal fine, with no loss of function. Hands that suffer a boxer's fracture will survive to fight again.

I could have handled this fracture by myself. I could have read the X-ray, slapped the plaster, and arranged for follow-up by a real hand surgeon. But this one was different.

This one was different, because the patient was Dr. Jernigan. He wasn't merely the chief of vascular surgery; he was legendary: Jernigan forceps, Jernigan clamps, the Jernigan technique for fixing ruptured aneurysms. His reputation was one of the reasons I'd come here for my training, but this was the first time we'd ever met.

The tech shot the X-ray, and while he took the plate down the hallway to the processor I did my intern's duty. I felt an extraordinary pressure as I asked Dr. Jernigan about his medical history, allergies, and the medicines that he took, acutely aware that my performance was being scrutinized by a person I hoped to have as my mentor someday. That concern was amplified by my recollection of the horror stories we all told about residents who were cut from the program for small errors at the wrong time. The very continuation of my budding surgical career might hinge on playing it by the book. I asked Dr. Jernigan about any previous operations and hospitalizations, any previous broken bones. Any prior injuries to his hand.

Dr. Jernigan was a thin man with salt-and-pepper hair. He was dressed in a cream-colored silk shirt open at the collar, and a pair of gray slacks with a sharp crease. I wondered whether he dressed himself in this casually elegant style before or after his injury. His uninjured right hand lay in his lap. As I observed this posture in a man whose hands were famous the world over, I thought maybe he felt the need to protect the good hand from seeing what had happened to the bad one. Dr. Jernigan maintained an impassive expression as he answered my questions calmly, quietly, in monosyllables. Then I asked him how it happened.

"Hit a door," was all he said.

I may have been completely competent to diagnose and treat Dr. Jernigan, but I was smart enough to call Bobby Tinglehorn, my chief resident, just in case. Within the first days of my internship I learned that Bobby was himself a semi-legend in this hospital for his skills and smarts, but mostly for his toughness. He could operate late into the night, park his ass for hours by the bedside of patients who needed the closest monitoring, and make others follow his lead. He played football for Georgia back in the days before the big southern schools were integrated, and small, scrappy white guys like him were the foundation of the Southeast Conference. My first day on the service, Bobby asked if I played ball. I simply shook my head no. I didn't think my experience on the track team was worthy of mention. Also during my first day, Bobby articulated the principles of intern success: "Keep your shoes shined. Keep your clothes clean. Keep your eyes open. Keep your mouth shut."

While Bobby was on his way down, I wrote Dr. Jernigan's relevant information on the urine-colored ER form. Those forms were the visible manifestations of the intern's performance. If the desk held few of the forms—if you were moving the yellow—you were doing a good job. But if you couldn't speed the patients through the system—if you couldn't get them triaged, treated, admitted, or dumped onto a consulting service; if you had an unsightly buildup of yellow forms—well, we said you pissed yourself. Piss yourself too often, *pardner*, and your status as a *stud-hoss* intern was in doubt. Maybe your chances of returning for the next year of your residency became just a little lower.

The swinging doors to the treatment room burst open and in came Bobby, followed by the junior residents on the service. Bobby strode across the cracked black linoleum, his face solemn, and he shook hands with Dr. Jernigan.

Then Bobby clapped me on the back. "This young *stud-hoss* takin' good care of you, sir?"

Dr. Jernigan's eyes closed just a little, and he made a tight smile while nodding. I was amazed at how gratifying it felt to receive that small expression of approval, that subtle endorsement of my thoroughness and professionalism.

Bobby directed the ER nurse to give Dr. Jernigan five of morphine IV. This represented a small break in protocol—giving pain meds like this before looking at the film—but if I could tell this was a boxer's fracture, then it must have been even more obvious to Bobby.

"Excuse us for a minute, Dr. J. I'm thinkin' you got you a boxer's, but I'll go look at the film with the radiologist."

He jerked his head toward the hallway, and I followed him out of the ER and into the radiology department. The rest of the team fell in step like baby ducks after their mother. We all wanted to be Bobby.

Bobby reached into the bin of the processor and pulled out the black sheet of celluloid. Then he walked behind the desk toward the main reading room, where the night radiologists stayed awake drinking coffee, doing crossword puzzles, and awaiting requests to interpret films. The radiologist on call was off to the left, but Bobby led us right. We stood in a smaller reading room covered with bank after bank of light boxes, almost all of them turned off. The wall of milky glass held dim reflections of our images. The stark white of my intern coat and pants, their crisp folds, stood out among the grayer, more wrinkled attire of my seniors. I felt like an oversized Ken doll among a squad of GI Joes.

Bobby slapped Dr. Jernigan's X-ray on the reading board, and the light sputtered to life. He nodded. He was right. I was right. Boxer's.

One of the residents in the room giggled. Another laughed out loud and said, "Wait until the rest of the guys hear." Each of them had suffered the sting of Dr. Jernigan's sarcasm on numerous occasions. To a resident who was struggling with a particularly difficult suture placement or a tedious dissection, Dr. Jernigan was fond of saying, "They *look* like hands. Why don't they *work* like hands?"

A glare from Bobby silenced everyone. Shoes shined. Clothes clean. Eyes open. Mouth shut.

Bobby ordered the rest of the team to return to Intensive Care, where they had been dealing with a pair of burn patients before my call interrupted them. There was some grumbling. Coming down to the ER had provided a welcome interlude for the boys that night. Nobody likes to take care of the crispy critters. They're a lot of work but never a source of good operations. Bobby gave me a gentle shove in the direction of the ER, Dr. Jernigan's X-ray in his grasp.

When we walked into the room we found that the cast tech had already laid out the rolls of plaster-impregnated gauze. Bobby instructed the nurse to administer a second, larger dose of morphine while he taught me how to remove a wedding ring from a swollen finger without damage to either.

"Take one of these long-ass umbilical tapes and wrap it round and round startin' at the tip, see? Then you come to the bottom? Slip the tail under the ring." He ripped open two envelopes of K-Y jelly and squirted them on Dr. Jernigan's finger as if he were applying ketchup to a hot dog. Satisfied with the lubrication, he uncoiled the tape in the reverse direction from its application, spiraling the ring upward until it pinged onto the metal table.

Bobby proceeded to pad and then cast Dr. Jernigan's hand and forearm. He reminded Dr. Jernigan to keep it elevated, to come back right away if there was any loss of sensation in his fingers, and to see one of the hand surgeons in a week for follow-up. Dr. Jernigan knew all this, but Bobby provided the same detail he would have given to any bum with this injury. Up until this point, Bobby had gone by the book, too.

Then he reached under the clerk's desk and came up with a manila envelope. He placed inside it Dr. Jernigan's X-ray, the white sheet containing the nurse's documentation, and the yellow form on which I had written. Nobody said anything as Dr. Jernigan walked out, the envelope wedged under his left arm.

After Bobby departed the ER, I caught up on other patients whose poor timing resulted in their neglect while I'd focused on Dr. Jernigan. There were a couple of drunks with head lacerations, normally good experience for medical students, but I sewed up their wounds myself in the interest of moving the yellow. There was a hot belly, possible gall bladder, that I sent upstairs for observation and maybe exploratory surgery. There was a minor motorcycle injury, no broken bones. I cleaned the gravel out of the soft tissues and scheduled him to return to the orthopedics clinic the next day.

The waiting room crowd was thinning out, which I took as a sign that the evening's action was drawing to a close. As I completed the suturing of one last laceration and began to anticipate a few minutes in the bunk, the triage nurse waved a yellow sheet at me. Sighing, I snapped off my gloves and read the form. Female, forty-one years old. Facial trauma. In the corner of the form was the patient's name: Jernigan, Julia.

On the stretcher in the minor trauma room lay a woman with an expensive-looking dress and a angry bruise on her right cheek. She didn't reek of alcohol like our usual clientele who presented with this injury. I knew the drill: Could she roll her eyes toward her forehead? Yes, on the left. No, on the right. An orbital rim fracture with entrapment of the muscles of the eyeball. A big deal. This would require an operation by one of the most expert reconstructive surgeons. The X-ray tech arrived with a special machine to image the complicated structures of the face and head. I called Bobby and gave him my diagnosis.

He came alone this time. Together we looked at the films that proved my impression correct. Only then did I show him the yellow sheet that bore her name.

Bobby looked at me. I looked at my feet. My shoes were shined, my clothes were clean, my eyes were open.

My mouth was shut.

It's always the nice people who get cancer, the cliché goes. Does that mean assholes die of heart disease? Jernigan was at the bank, making a deposit, when he clutched his chest and fell over, for what that's worth. His family refused an autopsy, and the medical examiner let it slide.

Hansen delivers the eulogy. I wonder which of the junior residents he had do the research. Whoever it was, he did a thorough job. Captured all of the great man's contributions to the field. Hansen goes on to describe what a warm and wonderful person we've lost. There isn't a wet eye in the house.

Mercifully, it ends. The audience waits patiently for Mrs. Jernigan to leave on the arm of her son. I don't know what he does. He didn't go into medicine. I would have known.

Mrs. Jernigan is almost past me when she stops for a moment, and I see a flicker of recognition on her face. She stares at my name embroidered on my lab coat and pulls herself to her full height. She makes eye contact. Long enough, but not too long. ౬

Hinges

Melissa Stein

You opened this door. Forced it back
on its hinges, drove in the thin wedge, saying

"I may need to enter at a moment's notice."
But don't you know that metal has memory, alive

the way rising dough resists a probing finger,
or trodden grass springs up against the foot's imprint.

Even flesh that retains the rare bloom of a bruise
soon lets it go. You keep these iron plates apart

so long they rust apart, flaking
into the slightest breeze, and still,

they remember what it means to rest
against each other, folded like wings.

&

Killing the Coyote

Anne Korkeakivi

All night he lies awake listening to the howling, and when Mark rises from the yellowed sheets of their bed at daybreak, he holds little hope the baby will be alive. The morning world seems strangely still, almost too quiet.

He slips his strong bare legs into jeans and swings open the door to the trailer. Mist is rising up from the hollow, obscuring the mountains that surround them. He can just make out a brownish form. As he moves closer to it, he hears a soft bleat then a louder one; the mother goat is still there. He pads through the wet grass to where she's standing. Next to her, staring back up at him through large dark eyes, the baby.

"Good girl," he whispers.

The kid blinks once, twice, a third time.

Mark would like to go back into the trailer to fetch a carrot or apple for the stalwart mother goat, but Lynn appears in its doorway.

She peers out towards the goats. "Everything alright?"

"Yeah."

"You didn't give them anything, did you?"

"No."

"Cause the mother has to eat only what's natural. I mean what's natural to her. Same for the baby. Only milk from the mother."

"I know."

Lynn pushes her lank blond hair back from her long face. "Mandela's awake." She turns back into the trailer, letting the door clack behind her.

Mark drinks in the peaceful scene, mama goat nursing baby goat, for a few seconds before following his wife back inside the trailer. "Hi, Mandy," he says to their fifteen-month-old daughter. She screws up her dirty little face and lets out a wail. Still, she allows herself to be nestled in his arms while Lynn prepares some muesli. All around them lay unwashed dishes and rotting bits of vegetable. Mark has abandoned trying to keep up with the mess his wife makes; no sooner does he start washing up than new peels and rinds appear. He buries his face into his daughter's blond ringlets and holds her close. "Do you know the story of Little Red Riding Hood and the Big Bad Wolf? Once upon a time, there was a little girl with blond curls, just like yours, and a pretty red riding…"

"I don't think you should do that." Lynn sets a bowl down in front of them on the table he made by sawing off the top of a large cable spindle. It takes up most of the living space in the trailer; all three of them sleep in the trailer's tiny bedroom. "All those fairy tales. They just perpetuate psychosexual disorders."

He lowers Mandy down to the level of the cereal and whispers in her ear, "…and they all lived happily afterwards."

Mandy shakes her head and shoves the bowl away.

"Aw, come on, honey," he says. "You must be hungry."

Mandy shakes her head, again.

"Please, Mandela," Lynn says, coming to sit on a wooden crate beside them. She smiles at their daughter and nods her head earnestly. "Look, food. It's good." She points to the bowl then rubs her stomach. "Yum."

Their daughter lets out a scream.

Mark picks up the spoon and forces himself to swallow a lump of the sodden mixture of oats, sunflower seeds, bran, and dried apple. "Yum, good." He flashes the brilliant smile that has won so many other people over at difficult moments in his life. Then, he too rubs his stomach. His daughter hides her head in her hands. He puts the spoon back down, gathers his daughter up into his arms. "Lynn, she's too small. She's too skinny. It's not normal. I'm going to get the number of a doctor."

"You're small. I'm small. It's genetics."

"Not that small. We're not that small. She barely weighs more than a baby."

"She is a baby."

"Lynn."

"A doctor will prescribe junk food. Cocoa Puffs and Frosties. He'll say give her anything she'll eat. Then he'll pat himself on the back for his cleverness." Lynn stirs the muesli and puts her hands out to receive their daughter. "Anyway, doctors cost money. They're all in it together; the government, the doctors, the insurance companies, the pharmaceutical manufacturers."

Mark sighs. He gives his daughter a final hug, sets her down in front of her mother, and shuffles back outside to use the shower he's rigged up round back of the trailer.

Lynn is finishing up a master's degree in Environmental Studies; that's how she knows so much about genetics and nutrition. She completed the coursework before they moved out to California. Now she's writing her thesis by correspondence. It's taking a long time because Mark is gone most of the day with his landscaping work. She's left alone with Mandela to care for, and the garden and goats. She grows most of their food; once the baby goat's done nursing, she plans to make cheese and yogurt too. It's time-consuming but it keeps their cash expenditures down while saving them, she says, from all the poison out there. Mark only buys bulk stuff like legumes and grain. When she's finally done with the thesis, she might apply to do a PhD at the University of California in Santa Cruz, in Environmental Toxicology.

Mark never graduated from high school. He got a diploma finally, but that was just because Mrs. Brandon, the registrar, had had a soft spot for him. "Alright, handsome," she'd told him. "Now you make good use of it." But he's never held any job where people cared whether he had an education. Certainly, no one asks him whether he took the SATs when he's pushing a lawnmower around their yard. It makes his head spin to imagine his wife with a PhD in biology. When she received a postcard last spring from an old friend now studying at the university in Santa Cruz, he was the one to suggest she pay a visit. She'd already mentioned its reputation.

This was five months ago. Lynn was sitting on a stump in front of the trailer, examining the picture on the card. It showed a lone surfer gliding in towards shore, dark and resolute among huge silvery waves. Mark tossed their daughter up into the clear canyon air, catching her amidst a rain of giggles. "I can take care of Mandy."

A pale yellow butterfly floated past. Mandy grabbed at it. "Butterfly," Lynn said. She took Mandy from him, checked her scalp and neck for ticks, and set her down on the ground. Mandy made off for the then-pregnant nanny goat.

"You won't be able to feed her," Lynn said.

At that time, Mandy was still nursing. Lynn had tried introducing homegrown carrots and radishes, unsweetened oats, and brown rice, but Mandy had refused all of them.

Mark dropped down onto his haunches and handed Mandy a long spiny pine cone. "She can drink from a cup. Save your milk and I'll give it to her."

"Pine cone," Lynn said to Mandela. "That's how baby pine trees are made." She stuck the postcard in her work-shirt pocket. "Anyway, we couldn't afford for me to go to Santa Cruz. We can barely afford for me to finish my master's. The United States doesn't believe in education. They don't believe in student loans."

That appeared to be the end of it.

But, after dinner a few weeks later, Lynn announced she'd written back.

She squeezed and squeezed at her small breasts for three days, squirting milk into a pitcher that she washed beforehand, then carefully covered and put in the refrigerator. She kissed Mandela goodbye and drove off in the pick-up.

Mark experienced an unexpected sense of relief as he saw the pick-up disappear down into the canyon. Being alone with his daughter felt like a test he'd, for once in his life, studied and studied for and was now ready to start.

The first thing he did was clear the sink and counter and cable-spool table, and wash the floor and dishes, with Mandy rambling around his legs watching. Then it was time to feed her. Unfortunately, with all the excitement of Lynn leaving, he'd neglected to crank up the trailer's generator. The tiny fridge had turned hot. Shortly after she'd drunk from her cup, Mandy threw up. Mark sniffed at the stored breast milk. He dipped a finger in to taste it. He spit the soured milk back out into the sink and rinsed his mouth with water. He dumped the rest of the jug's contents down the toilet.

He combed through the jumble in the fridge, under the sink, in the cabinet. While Mandy cried, he boiled up whole rice like he'd seen Lynn do, scraped dirt from carrots. He offered them to her, one after another. Mandy shook her head and cried harder. Finally, he put her on his back and hiked the four miles down to the canyon's general store and post office. He could have called Lynn at her friend's place from there—they had no phone at the trailer—but, instead, he bought a tin of formula. He also bought some hamburger and a box of desiccated mashed potatoes. Finally, he bought a cup of boiling water and a bottle of spring water. He mixed the waters together and added the formula right there on the store porch.

Mandy drank it down with a gusto she'd never brought to nursing. She stopped crying, smiled at everyone around them, and burped.

That evening, after he'd finished cleaning the trailer and sat down to eat his own dinner, she'd waved her little hands and babbled excitedly until he let her taste his hamburger and mashed potatoes. These were foods that had never been inside the trailer before. She gobbled her spoonfuls down and demanded more.

"Maybe she's got allergies," he told Lynn, when she came back and he'd had to tell her the story. "Or something is wrong with her intestines or digestive system. Maybe that's why she hasn't been much for eating the food you've given her."

Lynn threw the box of formula in the garbage and gathered Mandy up to her. She stroked their daughter's blond curls and asked forgiveness for having left her. But, the damage was done. Mandela refused to nurse any longer. And, with neither Lynn's breasts nor Mark's groceries to sustain her, she started to feel lighter.

The following night, they hear the howling again.

"I wonder how long it's been there. It could have been there for awhile." His voice drops to a whisper. "It could have been there without us even knowing."

Lynn lies back on the mattress. Mark can see splotches of carrots and buckwheat on the faded tank top she's wearing. Moonlight strains in through the hole he cut out of the trailer roof above the bed for a skylight, and the down on her naked legs looks almost fluorescent. It's all he can do to keep from running his hand over it.

"Tomorrow I'll see if I can find any blueberries," she says. "I saw some bushes up by the creek. She likes blueberries."

Another howl. Lying on the mattress between them, their daughter groans deeply, shifts. They both hold their breath, but she continues sleeping.

"Maybe we should get a gun," he says.

"You can't get a gun. You've got a prior."

Her words feel like a slap against his face. He doesn't bother pointing out that she could buy it. She's clean. But, of course, she'd never buy a gun, not even a shotgun, much less agree to his using it. "We gotta do something."

Lynn closes her eyes. "Sleep. That's what we need to do."

"Seriously, Lynn. Otherwise, the baby's gonna die."

"There's nothing for us to do."

"The wolf's gonna eat her. He is. I feel it."

Lynn laughs, a dry whisper of a laugh like autumn leaves. "Mark. There aren't any wolves in California. There haven't been any wolves in California for almost 100 years. The last one caught was, like, in the 1920s. Don't you ever read the papers?"

The unfairness of this remark hurts him. "You're the one against subscribing to a paper. Remember?" he says. But he doesn't want to start a new fight right now. Besides, they can't afford a subscription and, even if they could, she'd probably be the one to read it. He never read the paper before he met her.

So, he laughs too. "Anyway, not in 1920, I didn't. My mother wasn't even born then."

"No. I mean now." In the dark, her face looks tired again. "Now. They've been fighting over reintroducing them into the wild. They did it in Yellowstone, some in Idaho. They created a controlled area for them, down by the border. Mexican gray wolves. It's a great source of fodder for the politicians. Get to pretend they give a shit about the environment. About wildlife."

Mark doesn't want to get started on that now either. Politicians are one of the reasons they moved to the canyon. Lynn would have liked something even more isolated, Idaho or Canada, and only leaves their little canyon to visit one of the pesticide-free farms in the area or the general store to send a letter. He thinks their daughter should meet more people, but Lynn is dead set on home schooling.

"Well, maybe one wandered north," he says.

"Wolves are sociable animals. They mate long-term. They travel in packs. If they howl or bay, it's because they've been separated from their pack— or have been ostracized—and are looking for other wolf company. Or," she adds, shrugging, "cause they've found something good to eat and are informing the rest of their pack."

Mark sits up. "So! He's informing his pack. About the baby."

Lynn props herself up on an elbow and trains her level eyes on him. "Mark. That's a coyote. And, it's further away than you think and, if it does come here, no little fence you put up is going to stop it, anyway. Coyotes have managed to survive two centuries of being chased, hunted, trapped, poisoned—every nasty thing humans can think of. And, you know what? There are more of them than ever. And, they are everywhere, in the countryside, in the cities, in suburbs. They're in every U.S. state but Hawaii. So, you know what else? You might as well just get to sleep and forget about it." She drops back down on her back. "There's nothing you're going to be able to do about a coyote." With this, she pulls the sheets up around her chin.

Mark stretches out on the bed beside her. He listens to the sound of his wife's resigned breathing, his daughter's ragged snores between them; occasionally, a howl. "Sounds like a wolf to me," he whispers.

When Mark arrives at work the next morning, Manuel tells him, "You got a call from the Man this morning; I hear it over the machine. Say you come see him tomorrow. Eleven."

Mark takes a sip of the coffee he picked up at McDonald's after leaving the trailer. He knows it's an extra expense but bringing home beans to brew always provokes a lecture on South American colonial politics that he doesn't need to hear. Besides, it makes him feel better, the couple of minutes he spends every morning in McDos, out amongst other people on their ways to work. He's careful not to leave the Styrofoam cups in the pick-up. "Oh, yeah? What time he called?"

"You just miss him." Manuel hoists himself up onto the back of the truck, seizes a sixty-pound sack of soil and starts dragging. He stops to squint down at Mark. "I expecting big things from you, Boss-man."

Mark has promised Manuel, his best worker and the unofficial overseer of the landscaping business Mark has been putting together since he and Lynn moved out to California two years ago, that if the loan comes through he'll give him a two-week paid vacation. Manuel is documented, and he would use it to visit his family in Mexico. Manuel is the only one who knows about Mark's plans to create Gradiani & Co. Landscapers out of Mark's Mowing, with a fleet five pick-up trucks strong and an army of fifty workers. Mark intends to wait until everything's up and running before he tells Lynn about it. He's going to bring her a mug with the UC/Santa Cruz logo on it and stick a signed blank check in it. He can just imagine her gray eyes widening.

The idea brings him a rush like he never felt back in the days when he was still using. But, there's something else—he thinks it might be better not to tell her before he's got it all set up. Lynn hadn't acted impressed the one time he'd brought her to see the abandoned semi he uses as an office. He has a land line hooked up inside; it's the only above-board expense. The truck is parked in an abandoned lot: no rent. The guys work under the table: no insurance, no taxes. She took a look at the four Mexicans and two black guys squatting on the ground outside the semi, waiting for the day's orders, and pursed her lips. "These guys… how much are you paying them?"

"More than they'd get back in Tijuana."

"That's not an answer."

"Oh, yes, it is, Lynn. A good one, if you come from Tijuana."

"That's called exploitation, Mark."

"I'm giving these guys a break. A chance to earn some money."

"California minimum wage is $8.00 per hour. Do they have medical coverage?"

"We don't have medical coverage."

"I know. The U.S. government…"

They never discussed it again, or anything that he does away from the canyon. The trick now would be to get the suits at the bank to give him a loan without asking questions either. If they find out he's already amassed a crew mostly of workers without papers—that this is how he's managed to put away his little cache of seed money—he'll be facing more than a refusal. And, this wouldn't be a first conviction.

If asked, he plans to say the money is from his in-laws. Believable enough: If Lynn would ask, his in-laws could front him the money.

Manuel hops down from the flat of the truck and heaves the heavy sack back onto his shoulder. "You look nice tomorrow. Put on a jacket or something."

The last time Mark wore a jacket was for his first meeting with his future in-laws. He borrowed it. He's always wanted to have one of his own.

Mark has a few private dreams; having his own business, helping his smart wife earn a PhD, and building a decent home for his kid are the biggest ones. But there are other bits that splinter off, like the image of himself all dressed up, looking sharp. Good looks are maybe the one thing he has always had in abundance. He had liked putting on that borrowed jacket, checking himself out in all the parked cars' side-view mirrors as he strutted past—even if his friend's older brother, upon handing it over, swore to kick his punk ass if he got so much as one spot on it. And it had just been wide-waled corduroy, nothing stylish.

He wore a tie, too, for the occasion; the one his father hadn't been buried in. Then, he borrowed his neighbor's iron and pressed his jeans. She was a nice old lady, Mrs. Pantanello, never complained about his saxophone playing late at night or the parties. She even gave him some advice that day. She warned him to bring a present.

He and Lynn had met working on the same community project—but she was there as a volunteer and he was there doing court-ordered community service. With prodding and after quite a few nights of sex, she'd confessed her mother was a psychiatrist and her father headed a public-policy think tank. Mark's father hadn't left behind a penny when he died, and his mother worked in a laundromat. Mark had moved out when he was sixteen. He didn't even have a bed in his apartment. He slept on the floor on a mattress.

What could he offer Lynn's parents that they didn't already have nicer?

"Bring roses," Mrs. Pantanello said. "You can never go wrong with roses."

She didn't say anything about how he was to afford them, and he realized she must think he'd returned to nickel and dime-ing. But she was wrong; after his four-month stint doing real time, he'd sworn off dealing forever. So, he'd stopped at the Hendrick mansion on his way to dinner. He'd done grounds work there during summers, so he knew there were long-stemmed roses in one of its formal gardens. He stowed his motorcycle behind some elms and snuck in through the hedge. He wasn't that worried about getting caught; the housekeeper had always liked him. By the time he was back on his bike, he had a bouquet to rival any top-tier florist's.

Mrs. Gardiner, Lynn's mom, answered the door with a gin and tonic in one hand and a book in the other. She was dressed in faded jeans and an old T-shirt emblazoned with the words "Tequila Sunrise."

"Good heavens, come look at this, Larry!" she called over her shoulder. She smiled at Mark. "Where ever did you find long-stem roses with thorns still on them? What did you do? Steal them?"

"Yeah." He flaunted his most dazzling smile.

She threw back her head to laugh and a bit of her highball splashed onto her wrist. She pointed to his tie and borrowed jacket. "You can take those off now."

By the end of that evening, he felt as though he'd taken it all off. They asked him endless questions about himself, and he answered every one nearly honestly. He found himself telling about his father's death when he was twelve, his sorry school record, even about his stints in juvie and jail and how they'd led to his participation in the community project. "But, now, I'm through with messing around," he announced, and they nodded their heads and offered him more stuffed sun-dried peppers and Cabernet Sauvignon. Never once did they show surprise that such a handsome flashy boy would be interested in their pale quiet daughter and—after months of catching comments on the subject—he found it an incredible relief.

Of course, he managed to spill the red wine on the borrowed jacket. Or, actually, she did. Mrs. Gardiner. He assured her it wasn't a problem.

"Any sign of the wolf?" He throws his sweatshirt over the door of the bedroom, the only place where he can see a space for it. Lynn's school papers cover the spool, and the floor is littered with clothes and towels and the playthings he's made for Mandy. Dirty pots and pans and glass canisters occupy every corner of the tiny sink, washboard, and the top of the fridge. His mind races ahead to the time when he can build a proper house for them up here, with a deck and two bedrooms. He doesn't want his daughter to grow up in a repeat of his own childhood's squalor.

"What wolf?" Lynn is bent over a textbook, open to a maze of graphs and tables. To him, they could be scratches made by Mandy. He strokes his wife's thin neck. She makes a sign to speak softly.

"The one we heard last night," he whispers.

Lynn sighs. "That wasn't a wolf. I told you. There haven't been wolves around here for decades. Like everything else, they were killed off by our arrival."

"Us, personally? We did that to the wolves? We've only been here two years."

"Humankind."

Mark shrugs. He knocks a towel off a crate and sits down. It feels good to remove his shoes. He wiggles his heat-swollen toes. "Well, it sure sounded like a wolf."

Lynn turns a page in her book. "It was a coyote. There are tons of coyotes in these hills. Coyotes don't mind barbecues and cul-de-sacs. If anything, they like them. Easy pickings. And wolves don't like to travel alone. I told you. Lone wolf, that's some sort of rock-n-roll myth. In truth, wolves are herd animals."

It's hot in the trailer, too hot. Or, maybe it's just been a hot day for dragging bags of dirt around and pushing lawn mowers. Too hot to have to work at making room for himself inside the trailer. He kicks a pile of Lynn's books off the spool table. They burst open across the floor, but he makes no effort to retrieve them. He leans back, leaving his feet propped up on the table, right beside her.

As he was leaving this evening, Randolph, one of his two black workers, passed him the number of a doctor, scrawled in red on a scrap of paper. Randolph also has a baby girl and said this doctor sometimes cut her fees. Mark squeezes a hand into his pants pocket, withdraws the scrap of paper, and tosses it on top of Lynn's textbook. "Here's a good doctor's number. He takes care of kids. For cheap. And, we haven't killed off everything. Remember? Not the coyotes. You said there were more than ever." Lynn raises her head, and he looks into her face, shrugs again, and drags off his sweaty T-shirt. His torso is dark from the sun, smooth with muscle. He glances down over his body and feels better. He can feel her looking at it too.

"Whatever it is," he says. "It comes back—it's gonna kill your goats."

Lynn slips off her tank top. Her breasts are small as a girl's. "If he does, he does. Nature's way."

He considers pushing the question of the doctor's number further. But Lynn's there waiting for him, and Mandy is peaceful, sleeping.

Mandy screams for five hours that night. It starts when she wakes from her nap and continues until midnight. Finally, Mark digs out his saxophone, removes the sheet from their bed and uses it to strap his daughter onto his back.

Lynn frowns. "You're going to damage her ears."

"Well, we could ask that doctor about that too."

Lynn rolls her eyes. "Are we going to get started on that again?"

He shakes his head and heads for the door. "I'm going to put Mandy to sleep."

"More than five million children in the United States have some noise-induced hearing loss. Gas-powered leaf blowers, hair dryers, video games, guns…"

He steps out into the night and walks his daughter up into the canyon. When he's found what seems just the right moonlit spot, he stands still and starts playing his saxophone. His daughter stops crying, grabs his hair. She seems frightened. He lowers the saxophone and sings instead, until he can hear the ragged sound of her sleeping.

In the shadows around them, he thinks he sees angry pale eyes, shining.

The next morning, at eleven sharp, he's sitting in a fake-leather chair, wearing a smart new jacket.

"It's a good proposal," Mr. Crane, the loan supervisor, says. "In another economy…"

Before arriving at the bank, Mark stopped in at the Three Hills Mall. He tried on a series of cheap jackets of wool and polyester but settled on an expensive wool-silk blend, so fine he hardly felt it on his shoulders. He also bought an Egyptian-cotton shirt in a blue the smiling salesgirl said matched his eyes. He glanced at his reflection in the wall-sized shop mirror. "I'll wear them out of the shop," he told her.

"Economy's gotta pick up!" Mark interrupts now, feeling confident in his enthusiasm, although he has no idea whether this is true or not. He pushes away the memory of Lynn's comment about him never reading the paper. "Anyway, believe me: Good economy, bad economy, it doesn't make a difference. People need their lawns done, and they need someone to do it. Even with how things are right now, I've still got more jobs than we can handle. I have to turn people down daily."

"We?"

Mark starts at his own gaffe. "I mean, we guys out there mowing your lawns. I'm not the only one with a deal like this going. I'm just," and he leans forward, "the one with the best idea how to make money from it."

But Mr. Crane has withdrawn his smile. Mark sees that he has figured out where the seed money has come from, that it has involved undeclared workers, and he doesn't want anything to do with it.

"I'm sorry, son," the loan officer continues flatly. "I wish you the best. Thank you for coming to us with your proposal." Mark tries to think what to say to save the situation, but Mr. Crane is already looking right through him. He might as well be invisible.

That night, between the agitation of his daughter and the sound of the baying, Mark again finds it impossible to sleep. Twice, he gets up to check on the baby goat.

"Not dead yet," he whispers, after the second time.

A howl breaks out just that moment, echoing through the clover fields, the scrub, the patches of forest that surround their trailer.

"Maybe I could set a trap for it."

"Give it up, Mark. You can't do anything about it. Anyway, what would you do, even if you could catch it?"

"Ostracized? That's what you said? That means kicked out from its pack?"

Lynn buries her head in a pillow. "Yeah."

"So, why would a wolf be ostracized?"

Lynn groans and rolls away.

He gets up and goes to the fridge. Inside, blueberries are spilling out of colanders, plastic containers, and empty milk bottles. He glances at the spool table. The number for the doctor is gone. He hesitates then calls to the bedroom. "Did you walk down to the store today?" They have to use the pay phone at the general store to make calls. Even if they could afford one, cell phones wouldn't work in the canyon.

Lynn's voice sounds heavy with the effort of remaining patient. Or maybe it's with sleep. "Didn't you see all the blueberries?"

"Yes."

"Well, that's your answer." Her voice sounds further away now, like she's turned to face the trailer's wall.

No, that means. She wouldn't have had time to pick all those berries and walk down. And that also means she couldn't have called the doctor.

He grabs the garbage can out from under the sink and dumps it upside down onto the floor of the trailer. Discarded berries, Mandy's uneaten dinner, crumpled papers from Lynn's studies spill out all over. Amidst them, rolled into a ball but still recognizable because of the bright red ink, is the number. Discarded.

"What are you doing?" Lynn says.

The face of the loan officer flashes up in front of Mark, the way it had closed up like a series of doors. "I'm sorry," the man said, but his face had announced that Mark was already gone rather than standing there grinning foolishly in his new jacket.

Mark curses under his breath and slips out of the trailer.

There's a slight wind; cool, fresh. The lightness of it makes him feel all the more alone out there.

He sees them. Hollow eyes, gazing back at him through the darkness.

Something in him clicks, like the safety on a shotgun. Better, he thinks, to kill the goats himself. Better to just get it over with. At least he'd get some sleep.

Instead of turning towards the goats, however, he faces the trailer. He sees it as it is, faded white with a faded green trim, metal steps rusting into the overgrown grass surrounding it. Then, he sees it how he hoped to see it, transformed, a home for his family with a wooden deck leading off the living room and a little lawn around it.

He can feel wet under his feet; dawn must be coming. He strides over to the goat enclosure. He puts his arms around the baby goat and gathers her soft warm body in to him. The mother follows behind; the three of them make their way through the damp grass and enter the trailer.

Lynn is standing in the doorway to the bedroom. "What the—" she starts but he cuts her off.

"It's like a barn in here already." He lays the baby goat down at her feet and closes the trailer door. Then he fishes the doctor's discarded number out of the rubbish on the floor and waves it. "You don't want to call, I'll call. I'm going down first thing in the morning. I'm taking the day off. Maybe I'll take the week off also."

It's the end of something or the beginning. While at the market calling the doctor, he will pick up some more desiccated mashed potatoes for Mandy. He will mix them up right down there at the shop, if he has to. He will scoop his daughter up in his arms just as he did the baby kid, and carry her down with him.

The mother goat is nosing around at their garbage. Still holding the number, he pushes his way past Lynn and lies down on their mattress.

Moments later, he is sleeping. ౚ

Soul Bargaining

Regie Cabico

By soul, I mean the silver that God has placed deep
inside me. Its weight runs through me, schools of dumb
fish, complicated as tiny buttons. Deeper than the front

trousers of the tricks I have rolled with. I cannot toss
myself into the East River though my soul falls from

heaven in a shower of saxophone and smoke. I am
lonelier than the iron rails of this bridge echoing the rush
of taxi cabs and a good hand job. The moon is stuck flat

to the sky. The warehouses are lit by flames of vodka.
I am bargaining my soul for grace of crows singing between

neon and this darkness. By soul, I mean in a hotel room
where a man places his lips to your ears as if they were tiny
candles extinguishing the night with his kisses. By soul,

I mean God make me a wind instrument so I can toss myself
into the East River. The street lamps are howling for the first

slivers of light. By light, I mean falling off a bridge wrapped
in the arms of a God who knows your name.

8

A Distant Shore

Patrick Pfister

Light gleams off a silver stethoscope and my eyes roll in their sockets. They land on a maternal presence in a white lab coat. Morphine renders my thoughts liquid, but I am conscious that Doctora Seres now stands beside my bed. I search her oval face. Her eyes are dark brown and warm but, like a church statue, her gaze reveals nothing except compassion.

"Oliver, listen closely," she says. "No one who ever what you have—at the advanced state that you have it—has lived more than three months."

Her English is so impeccable I fear I am already gone. I curse myself for insisting that she speak so directly.

"You should prepare yourself," she says.

I am tempted to ask, *How?* but her smooth, olive skin wrinkles at her brow, convincing me it is a question she cannot answer. Then I realize the opposite is true. She is wondering how I can be fifty-three years old—a decade her senior—and not know the answer myself.

"Look back," she says. "Take stock of things. Above all, purge yourself of regret."

I feel resentful that she speaks my mother tongue better than me. Then a lance of pain sneaks through the morphine and removes my breath. The room becomes an underground cathedral, a grotto of shadows and stalactites. For a second I no longer feel my own pain. I feel the pain I have caused others. I wince, thinking of my long-ago abandoned wife and daughter in Chicago. Then my breath returns and Doctora Seres leaves the room.

Cora, the young hospice trainee, begins tidying up as if she were in a meadow plucking flowers. In her impetuous grasp, the cushions and magazines become lilies and hyacinths. She is like a younger version of Doctora Seres, a spring blossom not yet witness to rampant death. Recently hired, she visits the hospital each day to help prepare me for my coming move to the hospice.

She asks in Spanish if I feel strong enough to sit by the window, and then helps me make the journey there. Eight steps. A few days ago it was six. I look down over Barcelona and the sea beyond, pinpointing the *barrio*—perhaps the very seven-story building—where, just last month, I reigned as Chief Financial Officer. Once again I disbelieve events—early retirement, about to move back home to Chicago after sixteen years abroad, then a stomachache.

Cora sits in the chair next to mine. In three days we will leave the hospital and sit together by a new window in the hospice.

"Doctora Seres said I must prepare myself," I say in Spanish, and notice for the first time I have difficulty pronouncing the words.

Cora nods. Each day during my hour with Cora I extricate brush strokes that paint a portrait of Doctora Seres. Her English comes from childhood summers in Scotland, undergraduate years at Cambridge and a residency at Sloan-Kettering in New York. In my three weeks here, I have tried to imagine her as a young resident but I always see the molded cheekbones and steady gaze of a mature woman.

Cora herself is about twenty, not old enough to have many brushstrokes. She likes rock-flamenco fusion and has a new boyfriend as well as a new job. A newspaper ad led her to the hospice. Looking for money, she found a vocation. Or so she thinks. I doubt that her bubbly cheer will last long in the grim netherworld of the hospice.

When my questions peter out, she asks her own. As usual, they center on my foreignness and how I came to be in this room so far from home. In her young mind, the word *foreigner* seems to correlate with "lost soul." I give her my standard answer: work brought me here, a chance to drive a Porsche in the fast lane of an international ad market. She has seen my visitors—clients, suppliers, agency colleagues—and does not care for their Anglo-Saxon reserve. She observes their hands that never touch me, so different from her own hands that caress my forearm or rest on my knee.

Sometimes the morphine makes time leap. Suddenly I do not know if Cora and I have already discussed "purging regret," or if I have only thought about it. Then I wonder if another day has passed. Fearfully, I turn my head and see she still wears the same green blouse, the same fresh smile.

"I'm late for the hospice," she says. "Do you want here or the bed?"

"Here," I answer.

While light remains, I gaze down past fluttering palm fronds into a shrub garden where a fat gardener toils. My own time for planting has passed. Doctora Seres cannot be wrong; she has seen a thousand before me. Two thousand. I must do as she says: look back, take stock. I must even drop the lie I tell Cora about driving a Porsche in the fast lane.

Trembling, I summon the sins of a lifetime—avarice, infidelity, bold-faced theft, moral delinquency, and crimson wrongs without pardon. I recall how I left my wife and daughter in Chicago to run off with a secretary, and then how I left the secretary to run off with an accountant. Finally I left America to run away from them all. Or from myself. Sixteen years later—five in London, eleven in Barcelona—and I want to keep on running.

I break out in sweat as I recall other crimes: a kickback that slipped into an Andorran bank account, the firing of a bookkeeper guilty solely of occupying the position a vice-president coveted for his lover. I deplore stupid acts and mourn deceitful ones. I recall the time I could have stood up for a loyal colleague but remained seated in my cushy chair. I reproach myself for things I have done and things I have left undone and finally I hit a dead end. I don't know how to go any farther. I can remember crimes and turn them into daggers and jab myself with guilt but I don't know how to stop the jabbing and eject the memory into oblivion. I don't know how to purge.

Sometimes I dream in Spanish but as the morphine wears down my mind, I will probably lose my acquired tongue. In nocturnal battle my immune system generates heat, scorching my dreams. I see my daughter as an infant, her skin as silky as a rose petal, her blue eyes radiant with bliss as they gaze into mine. Oddly, I speak to her in Spanish, call her *cariño* and *hija mía*.

Then I wake out of the dream and recall how I visited her in Illinois three years ago, an unannounced visit intended to heal old wounds and effect a joyous reunion. She answered the door of her suburban home and we faced each other across the threshold. We did not even shake hands. A nervous husband waited twenty feet down the hallway behind her. Her eyes were the color I remembered but somehow darker. She was twenty-three years old and nothing like the little girl I had known. I couldn't believe how she had grown—tall and willowy like her mother—though what did I expect after not seeing her for thirteen years. She stood motionless and said not a word, but in her stunned expression I saw all the rumors that had reached me over the years—dreadful childhood nightmares and teenage tragedies, psychiatrists, Valium addiction, her mother's mental anguish—and then the door closed in my face.

The next morning Doctora Seres and Cora arrive together. Cora straightens perfectly straight articles on the nightstand, once again plucking violets. Doctora Seres reviews the scribblings the night nurse has left on the clipboard at the foot of my bed. I watch her. Her burnished cheeks catch sunlight from the window and a faint glow emphasizes her jaw. She is maternal but does not protect. Sense of purpose runs through her being like a hawser. Stammering, I finally confess I do not know how to prepare myself.

She looks up, setting the clipboard aside. Her eyes brighten. She repeats that I must purge myself and then adds with feeling: "Take hold of what has sustained you. Let go of all else."

Her church statue gaze makes me blink. My childhood was Catholic, I tell her, but, like this country, I became adult. No judgment glints in her almond eyes but she clearly distinguishes a life sustained by games and gadgets, pursuit of pleasure, evasion of pain. I feel forced to admit I have not been sustained at all; I have merely been buoyed up, as I am now by the morphine.

She reminds me that I have access to all manner of oncological aid: counselors, therapists, caregivers, priests, bedside companions who read poetry. An association called "Foreign Friends" can provide these services in English, if I desire. I reply that I have been doing business and running my life in Spanish for over a decade now and can run the business of my death likewise. My tough-guy talk does not even bore her.

"Do you know how to pray?" she asks.

I try to hide behind the morphine, but the question quickly surrounds me and flushes me out into the open where I tremble naked before her.

"Oliver," she says gently. "Let your desperation impel you."

Annoyed, I feel a sudden urge to remind her she is a doctor, not a nun, but then she leaves, and Cora and I sit by the window. Today, a grey haze floats over city and sea. Down below, the gardener trims bushes near a stone terrace. I feel overwhelmed but cannot tell if by emptiness or terror, or if they are the same. I try to comfort myself with the thought that my journey to the hospice is still two days away. In the time left me, it sounds like two decades.

"Do you have any regrets?" I ask Cora.

I might as well ask the wall if it has any children. As she ponders deeply, I wonder what she will come up with. Perhaps an impoliteness to an elderly aunt, or failure to clean up litter after a picnic in the park. Maybe, as a little girl, she once ran away from home. But then all my emotions combine with the morphine and a great weariness descends over me. My eyelids flutter and I begin to drift. Be careful what you run away from, I want to tell her. You might not return.

That night, I catch glimpses of lives I may have lived, if only. I imagine myself as a good father, who remained in Chicago. I comb my daughter's thick auburn hair and drive her to her music lessons. As she plays the cello, she smiles joyfully, free of all childhood turmoil. Tears flood my eyes and the room blurs. Then I envision pain until it becomes so real the nurse must enter my sleep and boost my morphine. I am poured into a cocktail world: one part Illinois, one part Spain.

In the morning, I feel thickheaded as I listen to Cora describe an action film she and her boyfriend saw last night. The aroma of strong coffee and toast from elsewhere in the hospital reaches my nostrils. I realize there are patients who can still eat. I myself can still smell. When Cora finishes her description, I pick up my questions where they left off from yesterday.

"Do you know how to pray?" I ask, wondering if I ask her to avoid asking myself.

At best, I expect a schoolgirl answer such as "close your eyes tight and talk to God," but she nods and says: "Empty yourself and fill with peace."

She has said it so matter-of-factly that I think I may have embroidered her answer with morphine poetry. In any case, I am left without a reply. I stare at her for what seems a long time and then my eyes begin closing again and soon I am alone in the room. A short while or a day later—I am not sure which—Doctora Seres and Cora materialize next to my bed. Even in my drugged haze, I sense something is wrong. Cora's smile is incandescent youth but her eyes reveal an adult effort to remain composed.

Doctora Seres looks directly at me. I wonder if her gaze on a patient has ever wavered and from somewhere in my foggy mind comes the answer: *No, never.* She tells me that I will leave for the hospice tomorrow morning. For a moment I stare at her dumbfounded. Then I plunge into panic and blurt out that I am not yet ready. I blabber half sentences and phrases punctuated by the words *regret* and *prayer.*

She listens attentively. Then she reminds me that the other day I mentioned my Catholic childhood and asks if there was a particular saint I was devoted to, or a certain prayer I might have enjoyed saying. Perhaps I could find sustenance in a renewed devotion to the Blessed Virgin, or in addressing myself to a figure such as St. Matthew.

Afterwards, when I am alone with Cora, anger invades me and I complain that Doctora Seres has no right to foist her religious beliefs onto patients. A burst of stomach laughter escapes Cora's throat and she loses herself in a giggle. Then she tells me that for twenty years Doctora Seres has been a Tibetan Buddhist. This sobers me and I experience a lucid ten minutes. Once again, I fumble in Spanish.

"What you told me yesterday," I say, "…about emptying yourself and filling…with peace…"

Eyes round, she stares at me.

"Well," I continue, "have you ever done it?"

Her head cocks to the side and she looks at me oddly, as if I am even more foreign than she ever imagined, as if the crazy things I say have no limit.

"Every day," she answers.

I am aware of my open mouth but can't close it. "Every day?"

She nods. "It's what I do when we're sitting here together."

"You…you fill yourself with peace?"

"Both of us."

We sit facing the window. Clouds have gathered over city and sea, thick clouds with streaks of black and grey. After a moment she remarks that it looks like rain. I realize I no longer know what season it is. I also do not know who Cora is. I merely thought I knew. I look down past the palm fronds. I recall the gardener planting seeds the other day—or was it the other month? I blink my eyes and somehow awake in bed. Cora is gone.

Bounce and sway torture my kidneys, rattle my bones. In the rear window of the ambulance, the clinic recedes. I glimpse palm trees, Modernist architecture, a bus of Japanese tourists. I am lying on a stretcher. Cora controls every aspect of my comfort, but I cannot believe the journey is only across Barcelona and not all of Spain. Buildings turn to trees; open sky appears.

I wonder if I will ever see Doctora Seres again and then realize the hospital is an endless runway. As I take off into the blue yonder, some new patient has just landed in my old bed.

"Almost there," Cora says, caressing my forearm.

I try to look up at her face but the angle is wrong or my neck is too stiff. I wonder if at this moment she is filling us with peace. Out the window, groves of willows and poplars appear, then a stretch of blue sea.

"Here we are!" she exclaims.

I awake in panic. Never have I felt so disoriented. The sound of wailing assaults my ears. Then I realize the bizarre surroundings are my new room at the hospice, not so different from my old room in the hospital. Just another place, I tell myself.

A few minutes or hours later—I am not sure which—Cora comes in. She seems older, more mature. As she inspects the room, imposing order, I begin to miss the old Cora who plucked flowers.

She wheels me down a dark corridor. Morphine colors flutter on the walls like tattered rainbows. We enter a community room and she introduces me to other residents, all women, all ancient. Cora explains I am a foreigner and wrinkled faces gape.

Later, in bed, I become conscious of someone cutting my toenails, shaving my chin, clipping the few follicles chemo has left me. Then an unseen force pulls me downward. I cannot recall who I was before illness and wonder if forgetfulness is the same as being purged. I stare at Cora. Her face begins to change, taking on the aspect of many women: Doctora Seres, the dowagers down the hall, then my ex-wife, who glares at me with fiery eyes, judging, condemning. Finally she becomes my daughter. Her hair slithers about her head and her face distorts into a grisly monster.

I gasp for breath. I feel my arteries hardening. I want to turn away but cannot. Seconds or weeks pass, and finally I reach out. It is only a few inches but I feel as if I am stretching across an ocean. I grasp her hand and squeeze. ಋ

What Bears Your Name

Nancy Naomi Carlson

for Matthew, who lived 13 ½ hours

In Haifa an old cypress bears your name—
planted from seed to honor your one day

of life—above a bay I've never seen,
no doubt blue as your room, your layette sheets.

No way to hold back deserts. Miles and miles
away, still they invade our walled-in heights,

our measured roads, our album faces pressed
and saved. I should have named you *Redwood*, made

to last the wear of centuries, each growth
ring a celebration of your birth.

Or *Air*—fickle, but true. This atom raised
in hand or floating through me like a wraith,

might have brushed an ancient olive crest
or tamarisk, or blushed you pink with breath.

℘

At War With General Franco

Luther Magnussen

A History of the Ebro Valley

Ever since I'd been ransomed back to my family in the fall of 1940, I'd been forbidden by Franco's administration to return to Spain. But in 1963 a friend got word to me that a manuscript by the seventeenth century historian Juan Candasnos Bédarieux was on sale in Girona. I'd long been an admirer of Bédarieux, and since my friend offered to set up a meeting with the seller, I decided to make the journey across the Spanish frontier. I had not visited the country since leaving the Falangist prison at Luicena twenty-three years earlier.

Hiring an agent was, of course, an option, although there were numerous problems with customs and the transferring of antiquities from Spain. But perhaps I was also feeling like I'd been getting just a bit soft during that particular summer, and I'd always hated the idea of the Spanish police preventing me from returning. Avoiding border authorities did mean a slightly circuitous route. I was spending time at my home in Cap Ferrat and had just acquired a 43-foot Hinckley Cruiser that a friend left me at his death—he owed me money and we'd agreed that the boat would become mine when the cancer in his kidneys finally killed him. The Hinckley was mostly designed for showing off around upscale resorts on the Riviera, but it was very fast and comfortable and I decided I could pilot it to the Spanish coast easily enough. My plan was to moor it somewhere off the beaches between Begur and L'Estartit, putting me only thirty kilometers or so from my destination.

Just before I planned to make my journey, however, John O'Hara unexpectedly arrived at my villa with the actress Kelly Maltre, whom he'd met on the set of *The Turning Point*, and they insisted on coming along. It was hard to argue with them, because they were clearly in the mood for an interesting excursion, so I loaded the boat with food and stocked the bar, and the next morning Maltre, O'Hara, and I set off.

The boat trip was exactly as pleasant as a person would imagine it to be, and O'Hara even looked the other way when I slept with Maltre one evening in the front cabin of the Hinckley. And by the time we were rowing the dinghy ashore just north of Begur, we were all well acquainted, having a wonderful time, and convinced that we would soon be returning with the Bédarieux and perhaps other treasures this particular manuscript dealer might have to offer.

We hitchhiked to the dealer's office, which was just south of the limits of Girona, and after a large lunch of mussels, saffron rice, a kind of steak that this dealer insisted numerous times was "Tuscan," and exactly three bottles of a white Villanueva wine, we were led to the basement of the dealer's building, where he kept his safe.

Most of what this dealer owned was not very interesting, but the manuscript that brought us there was exactly what had been described—Bédarieux's magnificent *A History of the Ebro Valley*. It was important to me for several reasons, but I mostly wanted it because I'd spent three months hiding in various places along the Ebro River after my brigade's defeat in the battle of Osera. After looking over the manuscript for just ten minutes, I agreed to buy it. I paid 30,000 Swiss francs—a remarkable sum in those days—and soon O'Hara, Maltre and I were hitchhiking back to the beach just north of Begur, ready to return to Cap Ferrat.

When we were back on the boat, as Maltre retired to the front cabin to put on her bathing suit, O'Hara confessed that perhaps he was going to propose marriage to her. I said that I thought that was a wonderful idea, although I still slept with her two more times on the journey home.

The Thomas Jefferson Brigade

In 1936, I joined the Jefferson Brigade after a six-month stay in Paris, where I was living with fourteen friends in a so-called *hôtel particulier* that my father had acquired upon the death of the Mayor of Limoges, a distant and childless cousin with whom he had always been close. At that time, my friends and I were very interested in mescaline (we had access to the synthesized variety) and we spent almost every afternoon and evening on various psychological excursions, carefully documenting what we experienced and then discussing it the next day over breakfast—always at Le Cannibale on the then-popular rue Delambre. It was a momentous summer, though, and while we felt that we were on the brink of something very important concerning the science of human consciousness, there was no question that Europe was headed down a path that would soon call us away from the internal odyssey we had embarked on. And so, when a strangely-mustached New Zealander named Barnett Hamilton joined us one day at Le Cannibale and told us about the brigade he had organized with other free-thinking expatriate friends, we all decided to join up, thinking that perhaps a journey to the insanity of the external world might teach us quite a bit about the human psyche as well.

And it was true that we did learn quite a bit, although it was very tough going at first, arriving as we did in the midst of the battle of Zaragoza. We put up quite a fight, and two of my friends from Paris died within the first hours of battle. I was very fortunate to survive, although I took shrapnel in my left leg and slept not a single hour during the three days of fighting.

The battle for us ended in the late evening of our third day in Zaragoza, when we were given instructions from a sort of socialist officer from Belgium to retreat to a nearby building. We were glad enough to retire from the hostilities, but we were quickly captured by twelve Falangist footsoldiers who had also sought refuge there. Since we were foreigners (and possibly important to them in some way), we were not shot. Instead, we were locked in a basement storage room. One of our band discovered a coal chute, however, and soon we crawled upwards, made our way across the city, and were back at the Jefferson Brigade headquarters in Madrid's Alto de Couso district. The brigade at that point had suffered terrible losses, but our leader, a British man named Thomas Craine, was doing an admirable job of boosting our spirits and promising that we would fight on. And despite subsequent deaths and intermittent imprisonments, our brigade stayed together for the duration of the war.

Interestingly, in 1959 I invited the remaining members of the brigade to my estate in Tromsø, where every year I hosted a party over the spring solstice. And in the spirit of nostalgia and common cause, we ate mescaline together (this time in the form of peyote buttons) even though most of this particular group was not part of the original gang I lived with in my father's house in Paris. Still, everyone embarked on the voyage together, and afterwards, over a dinner of oysters, a cold tripe salad, and goose cooked with raspberries, we talked with great warmth about our days in Spain and how, perhaps, we would never find such friendship and affection for anyone in our lives again.

The Calatrava Brush Factory

In 1937, after escaping from the Nationalists' prison camp in Sevilla, I spent three months living in the warehouse of a brush factory in nearby Camas, owned by the then-prominent Calatrava family. Luis de Calatrava was a rabid Falangist and off killing anarchists in Catalonia when I first sought refuge on his property, and certainly if he caught me there he would have cut out my liver, as was the custom in those days. But his young wife was alone and supervising the household by herself, and it was, in fact, her idea that I hide in the factory, since it was now empty because of the war.

I first met Josephine in her husband's bedroom in the north wing of the Calatravas' ancestral home. I was trying to steal clothes so as to look somewhat passable as I made my way to the coast. But just as I was trying on a purple Offenmeyer silk waistcoat—a fashionable item in Spain just before the Nationalist rebellion—Josephine discovered me and, after a long interrogation, offered her help. That evening she even performed alterations on her husband's clothing for me, the whole while regaling me with tales of the various tragedies of a loveless marriage, and, later, fairly shocking descriptions of what it was like to make love to a fat, aging aristocrat with a taste for brutality.

Her late father, she said, had been a reform-minded Republican, and had built the brush factory from just a tiny shop in the back room of their home. But he could not resist the allure of introducing the blood of a nobleman's family into his now wealthy but still bourgeois line. Josephine was his only child (although he had been married three times) and when she was sixteen she was married into the Calatrava family at the Cathedral de Sevilla, with the Bishop Arroba de los Montes presiding over the ceremony.

Josephine and I spent that evening and the next in ways that would certainly have put an end to her marriage (and her life) if Luis de Calatrava had ever found out. And after moving me to the brush factory and telling me to hide in the foreman's empty office, we continued our liaison with great recklessness. For the next three months we met every day. She brought me food—dishes made mostly of salted fish, tomatoes, and hard-boiled eggs—and after eating we were fast unclothed and together on a small horsehair mattress we'd found in one of the factory's storage rooms. After three months of this, though, the time at last came for me to leave. I'd gotten word through a Republican courier that my brigade was re-forming in Barcelona, and after several intense days spent in Josephine's company, I finally left the brush factory, tracking a difficult but passable route along the Guadalquivir River.

But our tearful farewell that day would not be the last time Josephine and I saw each other. I returned six months later, after escaping from another Nationalist prison camp, this time in Cádiz, and once again crept into her residence and surprised her in her bedroom. Needless to say, I felt a great thrill upon seeing her again. And Josephine too seemed to share something of my joy, although she also seemed nervous when she saw me. And when she hesitated at my embrace, I thought that perhaps she'd grown afraid of our arrangement, or even that her husband had returned. I discovered, however, after an unexpected set of stories, that Josephine's discomfort had to do with the fact that she'd taken a new lover—an American from Connecticut fighting with the Abraham Lincoln Brigade—and that he, after also escaping from the Nationalists in Sevilla, was now residing in the foreman's office where I had spent those three happy months, eating the food Josephine prepared for me and making love to her on the horsehair mattress.

Josephine wept as she told me all this, insisting that she would always have a deep and irreplaceable love for me. But as she came to the end of her story, she asserted that her heart now belonged to another man. We did, though, spend that night together in her home, and it was evident that she was very happy to have me back in her bed. All the same, the next morning she told me I had to leave.

Before I departed, she fed me an elaborate breakfast of eggs baked in olive oil, lentil cakes cooked with bacon fat, semolina and goat-milk rolls, and Castilian brandy diluted with mineral water and lemon juice (all in her room, far from the servants). In addition, I also took another of Luis de Calatrava's Offenmeyer silk waistcoats, a green one this time, and after a tearful goodbye, I was once again heading east along the Guadalquivir river.

La Nava de Trabanca

After the battle of Tragacete in November of 1938, I was imprisoned in a Nationalist internment camp just outside La Nava de Trabanca. It was a fairly relaxed camp, as these things go, and used mostly to detain foreign nationals and petty criminals who were not worth housing in the more secure prisons. These, by now, were being used to torture and execute the assorted Spanish anarchists, union leaders, liberal reformers, and communist soldiers that were most antagonizing the Nationalist movement.

Despite the fact that we weren't in the worst of Franco's prisons, however, the guards behaved with incredible cruelty, cruelty inflicted in an arbitrary way, often mingled with unexpected moments of kindness. For instance, the guards gave my barracks two decks of cards—an extraordinary luxury. On the other hand, more than one guard spit in our food before giving it to us, or threw buckets of freezing water on us as we slept. Perhaps the spitting and the freezing water were due to formal orders, but it has always seemed to me that people take as much pleasure from kindness as they do from cruelty, and that to think individuals only take pleasure from one thing or the other is something of a mistake.

During this particular prison stay, a month before my escape, I developed a friendship with a young guard named Jorge Teleno, who was very different from the others. He had been studying to become a priest before the war, and planned to return to his order just as soon as the fighting stopped. He was an ardent supporter of Franco—"Jesus has no greater champion here on earth," he said several times. But he also expressed dismay at the violence he saw, and, in Teleno's general behavior towards the prisoners, in the smallest of ways, he acted with a decency not at all common among the men who generally patrol prison camps. I also discovered that he loved to read, particularly philosophy and theology, and that he had a passion for the works of Francisco de Vittoria and Bartolomé de las Casas.

We had numerous conversations about these men, and about any number of other matters as well, and after many such discussions, I finally told him that my family was on good terms with the great theologian and scholastic historian Cardinal Moritz Wiedenbrück. I suggested that once the hostilities were over I'd be sure to tell the Cardinal of Jorge's intelligence and his ambitions, and that perhaps this would lead to an advancement for him. The next month, however, Jorge was called to Madrid to fight the Republicans in the Battle of Amusco, and (as one of Jorge's comrades reported to me) died two days after his arrival from bullet wounds to the head and chest.

Years later, at a dinner in Berne for the Peruvian Ambassador to Switzerland, I found myself sitting next to Cardinal Wiedenbrück. I spent nearly the entire meal telling him about Jorge, and his kindness, and the subtle turn of his mind, and his tragic and untimely death in Madrid. The Cardinal was very moved, although he added, after I had finished my story, that he believed that Franco was the most "misunderstood man in Europe," and that he had "always acted with the greatest intentions for his religion and for his country."

"I only regret that a man like Jorge did not survive to serve the General further," the Cardinal said. "But surely others will follow."

Of course, I didn't agree with this particular point, but the Cardinal was in his early nineties and not entirely lucid, and just as I was formulating a delicate response, I noticed that he was now lost in his Gateaux de Lausanne and talking to the person to his right, the great Austrian soprano, Angela Arnsberg.

Villarrubia de Santiago

Although the civil war ended in 1939, I didn't leave Spain at the end of the fighting and was hunted by the Falange for the next eight months. And in February of 1940, before I could make it to Gijón where a boat was waiting for me (my father had asked me to go to London to help set up a series of loans to the British Government), I was arrested by Spanish soldiers in the city of Albacete. Determined to complete one last task before my departure, I'd been caught in the process of delivering nine high-quality diamonds to the headquarters of a nascent Republican resistance movement located in the back offices of the Venialbo textile mill.

Once again, my foreign status made the authorities uneasy, despite the fact that they were killing everyone in those days, so after being intercepted on the Calle Caroch de la Sierra in Albacete's so-called linen district, I was not shot but instead taken to the prison at Luicena, which had long served as a point of incarceration for political dissidents. It was the last of my stays in Franco's prisons although it was also the longest. I was there for seven months, and buried so deep in the recesses of this particular structure that there was simply no means of escape. I did have two cellmates who made the time pass more easily. One of them, though, had suffered quite a bit at the hands of Franco, and his story was a constant reminder of the threats we were facing.

This man, named Ramón Camarena, had fought in the war alongside his four sons, each of whom had been killed by the time the fighting ended. He had a deaf daughter, however, who was still alive, and Ramón's only desire was to survive long enough to see her married—she was engaged to the son of a grocer in their hometown of Villarrubia de Santiago.

The only reason that Ramón and my other cellmate Carlos had been spared at all was because of their ties to a high-ranking friend in the Catholic Church, although before this connection was discovered, Ramón was brutally tortured. The guards knew of his daughter's deafness and, in an act typical of the sorts of superstitions that often play a role when one human being brutalizes another, Ramón's torturers took their cues from his daughter's misfortune. Ramón was first tied to a chair with a tin bucket over his head, and guards pounded on the bucket day and night with sticks and the barrels of their guns. Following that, his ears (or, more properly, the cartilage that makes up the visible part of the ear) were cut off with a pair of dull sewing scissors. Finally, his torturers seared his now just barely functional eardrums with red-hot iron rods. Needless to say, he was never able to hear anything again.

I heard this story again and again from Carlos for the next seven months, Ramón now only able to communicate with difficulty. Carlos told the story of his friend with a kind of magical terror, as though repeating it might somehow protect him from a similar fate. But we talked of many other things as well—Carlos interpreting the conversation for his friend with an extraordinary kind of pantomime—and as the months passed, I became quite close with these two men.

It was now 1940, though, and Franco was making a great effort to look as neutral as possible in the larger European war. Thus, there was some concern that holding wealthy foreign nationals in modern dungeons might not be very prudent. And so, in September, I was ransomed back to my father in exchange for a mahogany altarpiece carved by the Spanish Baroque master Gregorio Fernández, which he had purchased in 1924 from the Heider family following the then-famous Grundhoff scandal. My father had always hated the piece and had bought it only for the sake of my mother, but Franco apparently had a deep passion for Fernández and it was an easy trade. Interestingly, Franco approached my father seven years later, looking for help in negotiating trade tariffs between Spain and Switzerland. My father, of course, refused any such aid.

After Franco died, I was staying at a friend's estate in the Río Alberche Valley and I decided to visit Villarrubia de Santiago and my former cellmates, since it was only two hours away. Happily, both Carlos and Ramón were in excellent health and clearly prospering. As Carlos explained (first on the telephone and then over glasses of currant liqueur when I arrived at Ramón's farmhouse), they'd been released in early 1941 when their friend in the church was named Secretary to the Bishop of Salamanca. Following their release, they returned to Villarrubia de Santiago and, Carlos told me with convincing satisfaction, had done very well for themselves.

Ramón, of course, was still entirely deaf, but, as Carlos pointed out over my third glass of the currant cordial, Ramón had fulfilled his only desire in prison and saw his daughter married to the son of the grocer at an extremely happy wedding. And by that summer in 1975, he had exactly eight grandchildren, all of whom were boys, and every one of which was entirely devoted to his grandfather.

After staying for a long lunch that included sardines, a salad of oranges and roquette, roasted lamb, and endless plates of walnut cake, I returned to the Río Alberche Valley where my friend was having a party to honor the birthday of his ninety-year-old uncle, who had been a General during the Nationalist uprising of 1936.

La Madre de las Vicarías

In 1959 an art dealer called me from Antwerp to say that part of the collection of the Kolding family was to be auctioned the following month. He was in charge of the proceedings and said they were selling the so-called *La Madre de las Vicarías*, a tempera-on-wood triptych of the Virgin Mary. It had been painted in Madrid in 1420 by Fernand Luis Sollér, but left the country when it was purchased in 1876 by Nils Kolding, outraging and astonishing government officials and, of course, the Spanish Monarchy.

Franco claimed with some hostility years later that the painting belonged to Spain—that it had been stolen from his country—and because of these claims, everyone knew that Franco was certain to bid on the triptych and that he'd use the full resources of the national treasury to do so. For this reason, bidding from other parties was not expected to be aggressive, and experts predicted the painting would bring in between 50,000 and 75,000 Swiss francs.

Because the Kolding family claimed to hate Franco, however, and because they needed cash, they were willing to sell the triptych to me *ex-auction* for 150,000. They knew I'd find some pleasure in taking something that Franco valued so highly.

I agreed to purchase the painting and after the sale I heard that Franco was indeed furious—even more angry than anyone expected. The photographer Evan Vorau was visiting my residence in Geneva about the time I started hearing these reports, and, finding myself inspired by a set of prints he had given me, I hired seven prostitutes to pose unclothed in highly provocative ways in front of the painting while Vorau took pictures. I then sent the photographs to Franco in a large gilt envelope made by the Swiss paper maker Anton Reynal.

Franco's mystical obsession with the Virgin Mary was, of course, well known, and when he saw *La Madre de las Vicarías* in the presence of such scandalous behavior (and read my letter, written in my best and most formal Spanish, that the Holy Mother would surely see much more of this kind of activity), the reaction was as I expected. I received countless phone calls from assorted Spanish ministers and cultural attachés to protest my actions, each call insisting that the painting be returned at once to the deeply aggrieved people of Spain. Needless to say, I did no such thing, although the attachés and ministers suggested that there would be serious retribution for my actions.

Interestingly, four months later, I also received a furious letter from the scion of the Kolding family, one Gier Yost Kolding, telling me that, despite their own hatred for Franco, that he and other Kolding family members were themselves highly offended by the photographs and that this was not what they had intended when they sold the painting—a painting he said they all adored. He also said that Franco's fervent religiosity was something they all greatly admired and that their particular grievance with him had only to do with the fact that he had dispossessed them of nearly 2000 hectares of productive, arable land that had been in the family for 400 years.

It was the sort of complaint I had heard many times before, and so I replied in a short letter in passable Dutch that if their love for the painting was so deep then perhaps they should have made more of an effort to manage the family's finances better, and included in the envelope a photograph of John O'Hara vomiting gin and apple juice on his knees just below the painting.

The fact of the matter, though, despite these interactions, was that I did grow to love *La Madre de las Vicarías* very much, and although I regretted the photographs not at all, in 1975, following Franco's death, I gave the painting to the small church in Villarrubia de Santiago, where my old friends lived. ❧

Brazil, 1968

Claudia Cortese

> *In Brazil, the military regime gained*
> *a world-wide reputation for brutal and "inventive"*
> *torture of political prisoners. - Robert Cohen*

She thinks she'll be killed
but is taken to a hospital,
given a cotton gown

that smells of talcum powder.
On her nightstand, tulips bloom
from a crystal vase. Nurses take

her temperature, bring eggs
with yolks bright as coins,
bread evenly toasted.

One day a guard comes in and smiles,
It's time for your operation;
we're going to cure you.

Doctors remove her lips, sewing
shut surrounding skin.
A hole is cut into her cheek

so she can drink.
The woman visits my office.
She writes the story

on a piece of paper. She's lived
like this for years. I cancel
my appointments, promise

to do what I can. I lead her
to the back room. The surgery
lasts twelve hours.

I unstitch her mouth—
her teeth were plucked out,
two dog fangs forced into her gums.

It takes all evening to write my notes.
I don't have words to describe
the place where her lips used to be.

&

This, of Course, Is Spiritual

Matt Lombardi

When we discovered our professor had locked himself inside the fifth-floor bathroom of the Walcott building, we collected in the hallway and listened to him rant like a madman.

"Quivering thighs, the blood in poor circulation, my digestive tract piled upon the excretory system for hours as I finished *Gilgamesh*, first read Byron or *Self-Portrait in a Convex Mirror*, and Tate, Berryman, even an entire *New York Times* during the Iran-Contra Affair, cover to cover, and with a big red circle halo-ing my ass." I could hear him pacing around in there. "Of course, that was in my young adulthood before my physician warned it strained the anal and rectal veins. I did some of my best reading in the john."

Tom, the janitor, informed the class Professor Kern had resided there since late afternoon, almost three hours and had threatened Tom with termination if he unlocked the door or alerted any colleagues or authorities. So Tom stood with us listening and I swear it was a newfound loyalty, not fear of unemployment, in the way Tom held his mop beside himself dutifully like a rifle, the wooden pole erect, next to his ruddy face as it rested on his shoulder.

"I've never made my wife come!" The heavy wooden door blunted Kern's yelling, but the words held their motivation like the low fidelity of an old cassette tape.

A few students widened their eyes and shared open-mouthed grins. This brand of blatant expression had led us here in the first place, I supposed, all of us eager to write poetry as graduate work. Tom, who stationed himself in front of the bathroom door, pulled his shoulders back and straightened his posture as if he had just received military orders.

About thirty years ago an unexpected air mass of low pressure swept through the Northeast and May was cool and moist. The wet sky draped low over New Jersey. On the New Brunswick-Piscataway campus along the Raritan River, Rutgers Stadium was filled with damp people steeped in a relentless drizzle. They waited patiently without escape from the moisture. Women opened their purses to mists. The fedoras of elderly men and mortarboards of graduates were filled with perspiration. Humidity collected itself into fat droplets and spiraled down the flowered cones of tubas, mellophones, and trombones in the brass section flanking the stage. A mallet slipped from the hand of a bass drummer in mid-swing.

The damp university president took the microphone at center stage to welcome the crowd and praise the most recent alumni. He introduced the adored keynote speaker, "…A man from a humble Kentucky background, who left Vanderbilt University in search of truth. Honored not only by prestigious awards—the Pulitzer Prize, National Book Critics Circle Award, Bolligen Prize, National Book Award—but by the hearts and minds of this great country. And at such a young age he has not only taught in our cherished American universities, but has brought his knowledge to the small villages and big cities of Laos, Africa, Nepal, and Russia. We are grateful to read his significant words and are grateful that he is here with us today. Please welcome our nation's poet laureate, James Kern."

The audience clapped their wet hands. Students screamed their admiration. Kern walked across the slippery stage in a decorated robe, squishing along in his wet socks and penny loafers. He held the podium and leaned into the microphone, his wet hair matted to his forehead. Kern's deep voice came through the PA system and echoed through the arena, "Thank you President Bloustein, Dean Bellamy, Provost Wheeler, other members of the platform party, faculty, honored guests, family, friends, and most importantly the graduating class of 1971, to whom I offer my most sincere congratulations."

The audience applauded again. Kern applauded too, then waited for the lull. "I would like to begin with a poem," he announced.

He looked down at his wet words printed in a hardbound collection sitting on the podium. He adjusted the soggy tie knot beneath his robe, surveyed the immense gathering and began. "The—"

And as soon as he uttered this most recurring article of the English language, as soon as he released his tongue from the back of his teeth in conclusion of the digraph, the grim sky relinquished and its clouds rose from Earth dissolving as they approached a large sun. Kern was overcome by the instant and brutal blue of a newborn sky. The arid warmth permeated every cleft and fissure of the sodden stadium. The faint sizzle of rapid evaporation was audible to the silent audience, or so the story goes. They tilted their heads back and let the brilliant atmosphere gently cook dry their exposed teeth and limp hair. Eastern Goldfinches swooped in and out of the arena and the musk of the Northern Red Oaks had somehow navigated its way through Newark on a current of coastal air, giving Rutgers Stadium a fragrance its land had not celebrated since the pre-industrial era.

Kern looked down at his poem, then surveyed the crowd once again beneath the divine transformation. He leaned into the microphone and looked up into the sky. "Oh, what's the use?" he said and walked off stage.

The audience barked with authentic laughter. Kern was given a standing ovation. The audience cheered and clapped in the potency of spring.

Days later, Rutgers University's 205-year-old motto was brought to the attention of the public—*Sol iustitiae et occidentem illustra* (Sun of righteousness, shine upon the west also)—which further confirmed the commencement speech of 1971 as legendary.

A half hour before my entire workshop class had gathered around the door of the restroom where Kern had entombed himself, I had originally tried to enter that bathroom. That's when a voice inside chanted, "It's *ocupado*, please do not disturb. Iambic pentameter!"

I recognized the baritone vibrato as my professor's voice, although I had never known his moderate temperament to be so gregarious. I used the bathroom on the floor below and proceeded to class. I waited in the classroom with the other students. I said nothing about what I had seen or heard. I respected the fact Kern's bowels may have been uncooperative. This was not anyone's concern but his, and by happenstance mine. But after twenty minutes, when some students were deciding to leave, I suggested I knew where our teacher was. I told everyone to wait for a moment. In light of my brief encounter with Kern I felt obligated to do something. I left the classroom and walked down the hall with a half-conceived strategy: I would try to enter the bathroom. If our professor was not there, in the bathroom, I would agree with the other students that class was cancelled, thus fulfilling my sense of obligation.

I pushed gently on the bathroom door. It clicked to a halt against its spring bolt, prompting Kern again. "If I yell into the stall, my voice acquires a slap-back echo reminiscent of the reverberating effect Spector had Lennon use on his vocals post-Beatles. *'I, I found owoo-owt! I, I found owoo-owt!,'* Do you feel it?"

"James?" I asked in my most concerned manner, although I was reeling with nervous delight.

"Yes, Matt?" He recognized my voice too.

"Are you okay?" I asked.

"It used to be so radical to call your professor by their first name when I started teaching. I love it *now* as much as I did *then*!"

I waited to see if he had anything else to say, but I just heard him pacing around. Two students from class crept down the hall and joined me.

Kern's voice resonated, "Have you ever drunk from a tall glass whose beverage was on ice? And when you finish your drink or sip what has melted from the ice, you tilt the glass toward your face? The ice in the glass's bottom pauses for an instant as if poised to attack, then rushes at your face in one swift movement, sometimes punching your nose. It always startles the hell out of me, but I derive great pleasure from it as it is somehow always unanticipated."

The two students stared at each other. They looked worried, but also excited. Here it was. We had finally entered the authentic literary life.

Since our undergraduate studies, we had been an engrossed audience for writers who were teachers and teachers who were writers or sometimes for writers at readings. They would regale us with bizarre and impressive stories of the literary cosmos, the kind of compelling anecdotes that made us feel we were writing in the wrong era. Accounts of literary psychopathy, absurdity, rivalry, suicide, one-upmanship, unusual tendencies, appalling eulogies, financial jeopardy, contemptuous behavior, general hijinks. We heard stories about famous poets who locked other famous poets in chicken coops in one-hundred degree heat, while they slipped a piece of paper back and forth between the chicken wire for three days straight. The captor poet made edits on the paper and he continually passed it back into the coop, refusing to free the imprisoned poet until the poem was perfect.

Stories about our favorite writers bringing starter pistols to readings, drowning, sticking their heads in ovens, stealing each other's lovers and spouses, fist fighting at cocktail parties, committing crimes, becoming reclusive, accidentally shooting loved ones, soundproofing rooms out of paranoia. We traded these stories with each other, retold them at cafés and bars, thought about them while we wrote. And these stories, no matter how depraved, fanatical, or idiotic, were always pure heroism. Now, as we stood outside the bathroom, listening to Kern, we were part of the mystique, part of the lore of the literati.

"We drain the Varanasi and ship it to America in bottles to sell to the un-thirsty. Destroyed villages! Dead babies!" Kern shouted. "Where do the pipes in here go?"

By then the entire class, ten students including myself, had congregated outside the bathroom. That's when Tom the janitor found us and clarified the situation as best he could. We stood and listened, not knowing what to say or do.

"Have you ever opened a dark refrigerator with a burnt-out light bulb and felt intrusive because it is as though the food is dreaming of its future?"

Kern preached a barrage of disjointed observations. His sermons were short and odd, sometimes personal. We listened attentively, but gained nothing. Soon the class, with the exception of Tom, who warned against doing anything, began discussing what action should be taken. Someone suggested slipping Kern some paper and a pen underneath the door. Someone else suggested we call 911. A third student suggested Tom give us the key and we open the door, but Tom clutched the tambourine of keys clipped to his belt loop. Before we reached a decision we heard Kern ask, "Whose pieces are we workshopping today?"

We were silent, unsure of how to approach the situation, until someone answered, "Tanya's."

"The quiet girl who always writes in couplets about her dead grandmother?" Kern asked. "Or is Tanya the one who talks all the time and steals lines from Anne Carson?"

"The quiet girl," the Anne Carson thief said.

"Well, bring it to me," Kern ordered.

We collected our belongings and copies of poems from the classroom and gathered in the hallway. We sat cross-legged on the floor and looked at each other with astonished expressions. Those scheduled for that week slipped their drafts under the door. Kern conducted class from inside the bathroom. We could tell by the proximity of his voice that he was sitting against the door. Everyone assumed their natural roles and the critiques followed their typical pattern. The normalcy that formed around the bathroom door as class went on as usual was almost comforting, but there was an underlying thrill too. When another student walked by or a passing teacher gave us a curious look we just smiled proudly, which defused the situation. Any casual observer around here knew better than to question an artistic process.

When Kern dismissed us, it seemed appropriate we should depart as usual. After all, we wanted to think Kern was in full control of the situation and could release himself from the bathroom whenever he felt the need.

"I've always wanted to grow tomatoes on an urban roof. A field of them," he shouted.

We said goodnight to Tom.

On the subway ride home I decided I would come back early the next morning to see if Kern was still there.

I walked into my apartment eager to tell Arielle my remarkable new story. I couldn't wait to tell her about James Kern locking himself in the bathroom, raving with lunacy. I looked forward to telling the story in five years. I looked forward to telling the story as a published writer. I looked forward to telling the story as an aged professor to a rapt class of students who were eager to experience the unusual literary life themselves.

Arielle was sleeping on the couch in our small living room, cuddling one of her psychology books. The television was on. When I shut it off, she woke up and I told her the story.

"He's re-experiencing the innate need for self-realization," she said. "He's investigating the abandoned substance of his own past life and trying to integrate these materials into his existence."

I could tell Arielle was slightly turned on, either by my story or hearing her own voice in its aggressively analytic mode.

"Maybe his individuation is having a second coming," I said. We often read each other's work. The dry dissertation she was writing was a nice break from the overindulgences of poetry.

"Good," she said. "Or a third. It's an innate, continuous need. There's a tension between impartial, chaotic fluidity and individuated subjectivity." She pulled me down on the couch. "These dichotic qualities are embodied by the Dionysian and Apollonian respectively."

"Nietzsche?" I asked.

"He wasn't exactly the first, but sure." She smiled approvingly then rubbed the inside of my thigh. Her auburn, slept-on hair was half in her face. "Nietzsche argued that the perpetual, irresolvable tension between these two opposing aspects of nature cultivates the conditions necessary for the creation of tragic art. Your professor is definitely a poet." Arielle climbed on top of me and her large textbook fell to the floor. She unbuckled my belt. "And according to Jung," she whispered, "self-realization can be separated into two distinct epochs of a life. In the first half of our existence we separate from humanity. We attempt to construct our own identities."

I slipped my hands under her T-shirt. She was not wearing a bra. "I think he's lost his identity," I said.

She undid the button and zipper on her own jeans. "Well, he's probably already had two identities thus far. The first is the destructive teen-angsty one, which is usually expressed as animosity toward parents and other various symbols of authority."

"I know that identity well."

We kissed intensely.

She pulled back to speak. "I once slashed a tire on my father's Volvo."

"Me and Ned held our high school's mascot costume ransom. Sent an anonymous Polaroid of me wearing nothing but the oversized plush lion head to the principal."

"Jung also said we have a sort of second puberty that emerges while approaching our forties." She pressed her head into my chest and braced her bare feet against the coffee table behind her. "Which is when the position shifts from emphasis on materialism, sexuality, and having children to concerns about community and spirituality." She lifted her body slightly and slid both pairs of our jeans down past our knees simultaneously. It was an impressive trick.

I pulled her back on top of me. She slipped her underwear off and I followed her example. With one hand she guided me inside of her. "In the second half of our lives, we reunite with the human race," she said. "We become part of the collective once again. This is when adults start to contribute to humanity." She was rocking against me using the rebound of the couch cushion beneath us. "They volunteer their time for what seem to be worthy causes. They build, garden, create art–mmm–rather than destroy."

"But he teaches," I said. "Here, put your leg like this." She swung her leg up and pressed her heel into the couch cushion beside me. "He's been teaching well past his forties."

"But only teaches poetry. And as I recall, he hasn't written anything in over thirty years."

"That's true." I pulled her shirt off over her head.

"Don't slow down," she said. "The older one gets they're also more likely to pay attention to their unconscious and conscious feelings."

"It's resulted in manic frustration."

"Well, how often do you hear a person—uh—say, I feel angry, or, I feel sad?"

"All the time," I said and grabbed her hips more firmly.

"It's because they haven't rejoined the collective according to Jung. A common theme is for the disillusioned and frustrated person to search for their true selves and—mmmhuh—realize that a contribution to humanity is essentially a necessity for a whole self." She established a faster rhythm.

"Maybe he's been through—wow—maybe he's come full circle or is revisiting both stages simultaneously, merging them into this breakdown."

"Oh, yes. Yes! I guess that's possible." She was breathing more heavily now. "Jung proposes that the ultimate goal—oh, right, there—of the collective unconscious and self-realization—oh, *oh*—is to pull us to the highest experi—*oohhhhh*. This, of course—uh—is spiri-*tual*..."

"Yes, yes?"

"And if a person does not proceed toward self-knowledge—oh God—neurotic symptoms may arise. Oh, God! *Oh, God, Matt! Oh*..."

I opened the door to Kern's dead body lying before a wall of hieroglyphics he painted across the white bathroom tiles in his own blood. I opened the door to Kern's dead body lying before a wall of hieroglyphics he painted in his own blood and feces. I opened the door; Kern wasn't there. I opened the door and Kern was sitting on the toilet lid calmly going through his wallet, singing to himself. I opened the door; it was dark. I slipped my hand inside to feel for the light switch. I opened the door to a dense cloud of miniature kites jitterbugging above Kern's whistling breath. I opened the door and heard the soft cough of a collapsed sequin evening gown. I opened the door, "Surprise!" I opened the door, the last days of the Byzantine Empire pungent and choking. I opened the door slowly, the way we release our hands from prayer's gesture. I opened the door and Kern was drinking from the sink's faucet. I opened the door and observed Francesca's cracked mural, the first pregnant depiction of the Madonna. I opened the door. Arielle was standing there. I opened the door to neighborhood lawns humiliated by their eczema. I opened the door; drawn shades plaqued the handfuls of twinkling teeth tossed into the skyline. I opened the door. Kern was sitting on the floor across from Tom, who was sharpening the end of his mop stick with a machete. I opened the door. ஐ

Nabokov Attempts a Doublet at Seventy-four

Patricia Lockwood

> *To my mother, though, this all seemed quite normal. The matter came up, one day in my seventh year, as I was using a heap of old alphabet blocks to build a tower. I casually remarked to her that their colors were all wrong. We discovered then that some of her letters had the same tint as mine...*
>
> — Vladimir Nabokov, *Speak, Memory*

It is a puzzle, my son tells me; it will keep my brain
from uncurdling into childish milk too soon. Replace
the letters of one word until another word appears.
He writes, "Head to heal to teal to tell to tall to Tail."
Now he wants me to change a *flute* into a *cello*, but this
is impossible. I cannot make a cello out of pale blue,
yellow, and white, even if I slur the word. And I never do.

I open the Sunday paper, and it asks me to transform
moth into *bush*. The alphabet dresses—*h* wraps a shoelace
around her shoulders like a stole; *n* rolls in oatmeal; *f* makes
a loincloth out of alder leaves—and I sharpen a pencil.
The moth is almost certainly an elephant hawk-moth,
given the downy pink of the *m* and the unripe green
of the *t*. The bush is three gray branches of a Russian
sh, the bronze leaves of a *u*, and the rust red fire of a *b*.

"I solved one," I tell my son, triumphant even as the moth
fades to vulgar lace in the smoke above the bush. He squints
at my handwriting, shakes his head, and sings, "Head to heal to teal..."
There is no color. My mother is dead, the gift has not passed on.

ॐ

The Death of the Magician

David Wagoner

He found coins in our ears
and picked flowers from our hair.

He turned nothing to something and
nearly anything to nothing.

His assistants all changed places.
His animals disappeared,

and though we didn't believe
in what he'd done before

our very eyes could look
in the right direction, we

had learned to love his tricks.
Then suddenly he vanished.

We're all sitting here hoping
he'll reappear some day

from a locked box or a cage
or from behind the scenes.

We don't want to trust our eyes
or have to deceive ourselves.

We want him to saunter down
the aisle with his arms outstretched

for applause and leap onstage,
spot-lit, as brilliant as ever,

in charge of all we see,
and fool us over again.

ॐ

In Kalvarija Father Died

Itzhak Kronzon

In the year 1934, several months after my parents immigrated to Palestine from Lithuania, a postal worker of the British Mandatory Postal Service rang the doorbell of their rented one-bedroom flat in Haifa and handed them a telegram. In those days, most residents of Haifa had no telephones, and telegrams were sent solely in connection with either joyful events or bad news. Since joyful events were usually known of long in advance, both my parents understood that this telegram was dealing with a death. Grandfather Itzhak from Kaunas (Kovno), my mother's father, and Grandfather Shmuel from Kalvarija, my father's father, were then in their sixties, and both, like many Jewish men in Lithuania, were no strangers to sickness: heart disease, kidney disease, diabetes, high blood pressure. Father, who opened the envelope and read the contents of the single sentence, had to relay the bad news in such a way that, from the start, it would be clear to my mother, who was then pregnant with her first child, that her father was well. Had he begun the sentence with the word "notify" or "father" or "yesterday" or "died," she would believe, even for a splinter of a second, that the reference was to her father, and then, she might possibly faint or God-forbid miscarry. But one as wise and sensitive as my father would never let this happen. He looked at her and said quietly, "In Kalvarija Father died."

Mother did not faint nor did she miscarry, and my older brother, Shmuel, was named after that grandfather. Several years later, the telegram arrived announcing the death of Grandfather Itzhak from Kaunas, and I was named in his memory. Every time Mother would sing my father's praises, she would inevitably arrive at the famous key sentence "In *Kalvarija* Father died," while accentuating the word "*Kalvarija*," as her eyes and ours filled with tears.

Kalvarija is situated on the border of Lithuania and Eastern Prussia, located on the crossroads between St. Petersburg and Berlin. My father's family had lived there for more than two hundred years. At the end of the nineteenth century, the town boasted ten thousand residents, eight thousand of whom were Jews. Every Jew in Kalvarija (and even many of the Gentiles) spoke six languages: Lithuanian, the language of the peasants; Russian, the language of the country's rulers; Polish, the language of other conquerors who also ruled over Lithuania at one time or another; German, the language of the many travelers who stayed for the night, as well as the international language of trade; Yiddish, the language of the Eastern European Jews; and Hebrew, not only the language of prayer, but also the language used to educate children in the homeland of Abraham Mapu and the Haskalah ("enlightenment") movement that followed.

On Fridays, during the Kiddush, it was customary to speak only in the holy tongue, and when the need arose, orders would be given to the Gentile servant in using the Hebrew word for maid: "*Shifcha,* bread!" "*Shifcha,* knife!" Over time, many of these expressions became part of the vocabulary of the local Lithuanian women who would call each other *"Shifcha"* with correct emphasis on the final syllable.

Kalvarija also housed the insane asylum in which hundreds of mentally ill patients from across Lithuania were hospitalized. This was the largest source of income for the town's residents, who provided nursing care, services, and supplies to the asylum. I know that Father, most of whose brothers and sisters were physicians, visited there on many occasions. Throughout our childhood, he forbade us from balancing a fork or spoon on our finger since all the insane of Kalvarija would perform such balancing exercises during meals. I also recall a story he told us once, before bedtime, how when the Germans entered the town at the start of the First World War, it was decided to evacuate the insane and convert the buildings into barracks. One crazy old man, who had been hospitalized since his youth, refused to be evacuated. He argued to the director that since everyone knew where he had been until then, he would be unable to provide for himself. The asylum director decided to give him a certificate in which it was declared that the person named in the certificate is normal. "Thus," Father said in response to our laughter, "there was only one man in Kalvarija who carried a certificate attesting to his normalcy."

When the Germans left in 1918, Lithuania became an independent state for the first time since 1795. The League of Nations (a predecessor, of sorts, of the United Nations), which granted Lithuania and the other Baltic countries, Latvia and Estonia, their independence, required that all minorities in these countries would be granted full autonomy, including freedom of religion and education. Hence, there came to be established, during those few years of independence, a network of Jewish schools in which all studies were conducted in Hebrew. Throughout his lifetime, my father was more fluent in Hebrew than his Israeli-born children. I still keep in my possession the certificates from the Regional Hebrew High School in Mariampole, from which he graduated with honors, as well as the photograph of the Bar Kochva regiment, Kalvarija branch, in which he stands, at age twelve, third in the upper row, bearing an amazing resemblance to one of the grandchildren who would be born in Israel fifty years later. When we celebrated the Passover Seder at home, in Haifa, together with Father's sister, who had immigrated to Israel before him, they sang all the songs in the Kalvarijan Jewish version. Any attempts by Mother and her sister to sing the Kovno Jewish version were always met with dismissal, and sometimes, when he was more relaxed, Father would imitate, in a high-pitched voice, their dull and monotonous version. Even we, the children, preferred the rich and melodic Kalvarijan melody. On the Seder eve, Father used to say that all of Kalvarija sang "*Adir Hoo*" and "*Ki Lo Yaeh*" simultaneously. Eight thousand Jews.

I know that, in his youth, Father was a true Lithuanian patriot. He loved that country and its vistas, and would sorrowfully compare them with the views seen in overheated Palestine. Once, when we took a trip to the Galilee, he pointed to the Jordan river and said with a sigh: "A small trickle of urine and the entire world becomes excited and sings songs in praise. In Lithuania, there was a river called the Nieman, ten times wider and twenty times longer, and no one was impressed or said anything."

When he completed his studies in electrical engineering at Prince Vytautus the Great University in 1930, Father was drafted for mandatory military service in the Lithuanian army and became a flight engineer in their air force, which he called "The Aviatzia." He flew canvas and wooden biplanes above the skies of Europe, reaching as far as Tangiers in North Africa, a journey documented by photos and papers that I keep with me. I recall him telling me that one of the other pilots brought a monkey back from Africa. During the Lithuanian Independence Day parade, the monkey jumped onto the shoulder of the air force commander, removed the commander's cap and smeared his pate with toothpaste.

When he completed his service, Father contemplated an academic career and applied for the post of lecturer in electrical engineering at the same university from which he'd graduated at the top of the class several years earlier. The interview was a success. "There is no doubt," he was informed by the chairman of the academic committee, "that you are the most suitable candidate, but unfortunately, we already have one Jew."

Father was insulted and decided to leave this country that would not permit him to be a citizen with equal rights, in his opinion. His family tried to convince him to stay and not give up on the benefits offered by a modern, established country, and a well-to-do and educated family. But he stood his ground and together with my mother, who was already pregnant, traveled to Palestine, where they lived together for many years until their deaths in 1978.

The rest is a chronicle of destruction of Lithuanian Jewry. With the German invasion in 1941, the Lithuanian Gentiles rose up and killed most members of our family, and there was no one left who would send us a telegram about it. In Kalvarija, not one Jew remained.

Several months ago, in my home in New York, I looked up our family name on the *Yad Vashem* website. In this archive, it is possible to locate copies of original forms that had been submitted, in the 1950s, by relatives and acquaintances of those who perished in the Holocaust. Among these I found tens of forms that reported Kronzons who had been murdered in Kalvarija and about whom I had never heard. Many of these forms had been completed by Father, in his handwriting, and bore his signature. Thus I received a sort of greeting in writing from him, many years after his death. I, myself, do not have what is currently referred to as "second generation Holocaust complex." My parents were no longer there when it happened, and even their parents died of natural causes.

Owing to my specialty in echocardiography, I am often invited to teach and lecture in various countries. Last year, following a series of lectures in one of the countries of Western Europe, a delegation of five young Lithuanian cardiologists showed up at my hotel, wishing to invite me to Kaunas to teach the physicians there various techniques related to my specialty. I was frightened and refused. I told them about my uncle Leibush, a physician in Kalvarija who decided to inject his wife, his two daughters, and himself with poison as the Lithuanian peasants were breaking into their home to murder them; and about my uncle Abrasha, also a physician, whose wife and three children were burned alive; and about my aunt Jenia, who perished there with her husband; and also about my father, who had been rejected by Prince Vytautus the Great University where there was already one Jew (who, by the way, also died in the Holocaust).

The Lithuanian physicians listened with great sorrow to the terrible story, and said, not without justice, that all this had occurred many years prior to their births, and that, if indeed I would agree to come to Lithuania, I would see for myself that it is a pleasant and receptive country. Since I did not wish to hurt them further, we agreed that I would consider their offer.

When I returned home, I called my cousin in Israel. He was twelve years old at the time of the German invasion, and had miraculously survived the Holocaust, escaping the fate of 95% of the Jewish population of Lithuania. My cousin, now almost eighty years old, but still hearty of strength, mind, and spirit, advised me to go there, "even if only to show them that we are still here." Meanwhile, I received an invitation from the current provost of Prince Vytautus the Great University in Kaunas, who had heard my story from the young Lithuanian cardiologists, and therefore decided to grant me, in a ceremony to be held in Lithuania, an honorary degree in memory of my father who had been "....rejected by the University because of unjust prejudices."

At the conclusion of all the lectures, visits, professional events, and ceremonies in Lithuania, we departed for a trip in a limousine hired for us by our gracious hosts, who spared no cost and effort to make our stay as pleasant, enjoyable and interesting as possible. Traveling with me was my brother, Giora, four years my junior, and my sister-in-law, Nira, who had arrived especially for this occasion from Israel, as well as our guide Regina. Regina, who lives in Vilnius, is the daughter of a Jewish father and Lithuanian mother. She speaks up-to-date Hebrew and fluent English. She makes her living from the abundant ancestry trips embarked upon by Israelis and Jews from the United States, Australia, and South Africa (nations to where many Lithuanians emigrated prior to the First World War). She had acquired her Hebrew attending university in Israel years ago. She'd even attempted to obtain citizenship there, but was denied since her mother was not Jewish. Regina is a true expert on towns, cemeteries, and Holocaust sites. She carries around a satchel with a Lithuanian phonebook from 1939, containing the addresses and telephone numbers of many members of my family who had ceased to answer any phone calls a short time later.

Right around noon, we got off the main road and turned toward Kalvarija, now a sleepy and pitiful border town. Since Lithuania gained entry into the European Union, young persons are leaving the towns and moving either to the cities or abroad. Today, less than one thousand people remain in Kalvarija. The insane asylum is empty. The houses are decrepit. Many of them had been built of wood and appear about to collapse. The yards are unkempt, with scattered rubbish and furniture fragments, with chickens and pigs roaming amongst them. The unpaved side streets are empty. From time to time, a black-clad peasant is seen crossing the main road.

The main intersection houses the sole traffic light in the town. On the southeastern side of the intersection stands a single two-story stone house on whose roof flies the Lithuanian flag. On the first floor is a bank, with an ATM that faces the street. The second floor houses the town offices and regional administration. This is the house of Grandfather Shmuel. Once he lived there with his wife, Grandmother Chaya, and their six children. In the yard was the family business for the sale of agricultural machinery. The house was full of life and light. Each child had his own room, and in one of these my father would play his violin, as can be seen in a photograph that we have hung on the wall in our house in New York. Once, upon returning from a soccer match at the Jewish sports club, Father, who was sixteen years old, was so thirsty that he picked up and drank an entire jug of cream (we heard this story on numerous occasions during the rationing days in the 1950s, when we were permitted only one teaspoon of sour cream once a month). I also remember, from stories, the cat they used to have then. Once, when Grandmother Chaya stepped on the cat's paw and he leapt up and meowed loudly, she admonished him: "That will teach you not to walk around barefoot." It sounds funnier in Yiddish, but I don't know how to write it…

What remained of the large synagogue has been abandoned and partly demolished, but it is still possible to make out the Star of David on its façade. The Jewish cemetery is located in the confines of the local power station. The few graves that are there are covered by thick weeds and the tombstones have been uprooted and scattered haphazardly. Even if one tries with all one's might it is impossible to imagine how eight thousand Jews sang here together "*Ki Lo Yaeh, Ki Lo Naeh.*"

Slightly west of the intersection stands a restaurant which Regina claims serves the most amazing food. We are not surprised that the food there has the same appearance and taste of the food that we ate at our parents' home in Haifa.

Upon leaving the town, I remind myself and my brother that in all of our family history, we are the first generation not born here, and contrary to many other families, we are also not the last generation to die here. In my heart of hearts I also thank the chairman of the tender committee of Prince Vytautus the Great University, as a result of whose decision *my* father did not die in Kalvarija. &

Translated from the Hebrew by Iris Karev (Kronzon)

Father's First Heart Attack

Hal Sirowitz

Father said he felt this tightening
of his chest as if God suddenly
shortened his shirt collar. Air
was all around him but not
a breath of it could he breathe.
He had seen actors pretending
to have heart attacks on TV,
so he knew what was happening.
But he couldn't get the dramatics
right. Even though his was
the real thing, it paled compared
to TV. His son-in-law called
for an ambulance. He survived.
If he ever gets a second one, he
hopes it'll be more TV-like.
He wants to die like a professional.

&

Avoiding Rigidity

Hal Sirowitz

'It's the medicine that makes me shake,
not the disease,' I said. 'Then why
take it?' she said. 'If I stopped, I
wouldn't be able to walk,' I said.
'My body would become rigid.'
'Rigidity seems better than
all that shaking you do,'
she said. 'I'd rather shake
than not be able to move,'
I said. 'Each to his own,'
she said. 'But if you were rigid,
I wouldn't have to worry
about you accidentally
hitting me on the head.' 'But if I
couldn't move,' I said, 'what
would we do to make time pass?'
'We'd do nothing,' she said. 'We do that, anyway.'

છ

The Consolation of Anatomy

Kurt Magsamen

Cadavers don't look much like anatomy drawings. They don't smell much like anatomy books. The drawings are clean, ordered, the striations of muscle cells combed out tight and smooth, like the strings of a harp. The nets of veins, nerves, and lymph nodes have been lifted out and colored blue, red, pale yellow, and black. Some drawings are not in books but are posters of skinless athletes posing in the gym reaching up one hand and tipping back a toe to make visible the Brachialis, Brachioradialis, and Extensor carpi radialis longus muscles. Their muscles are a beautiful red, more like the red of lipstick than the blackened red of blood on a floor or the purple of blood puddled beneath the skin. The models of anatomy have wide eyes staring out that cannot follow strangers walking past. They are calm in their exposing repose. Cadavers too are calm but much more muddled, and everything is obscured by fat. Press a blade through the skin and fat will emerge, not the clean white fat of cattle, but the jaundiced globules that fall away and stick to the steel slab, and if the slab is warm enough, melt there.

It was that cold, yellow color that made me think my dad was half cadaver. His skin had gone yellow, translucent, waiting to cool and coagulate. A fall had put him there. He'd fallen on his head, his face really, and below his eye was a bruise so swollen and purple it looked as if a spoiled plum rolled beneath his skin. But his neck was broken too.

Gray's Anatomy: "The anterior cerebrospinal fasciculus which is usually small, but varies inversely in size with the lateral cerebrospinal fasciculus. It lies close to the anterior median fissure." Four vertebrae were crushed. Wait until he comes to. Then we'll know more.

Latin is so much like a prayer. *In Nomine Patris.* The extent to which the fibers of the ventral cerebrospinal, *Et Fílii,* cross in the cord is open to question. *Et Spíritus Sancti,* the influence of the motor cortex is preponderantly contralateral, there is a slight ipsilateral effect. There was brain damage. That's called contracoup from the brain bouncing around within the skull. Again, there is Gray's: "Its posterior surface is received into the fossa between the hemispheres of the cerebellum, and the upper portion of it forms the lower part of the floor of the fourth ventricle." My Dad and I were close enough to have talked about life and death, and we both agreed never to let the two mix, not for ourselves, or each other.

So I wait for the gap to close and dread what I may do. Where are the combed tight lines to show us? Where is the man in the robe speaking Latin? "Other fibers conducting proprioceptive impulses pass upward in the dorsal spinocerebellar fasciculus." Or am I left with the advice of my good buddy, Vladimir Nabokov, who once told me, "The cradle rocks above the abyss, and common sense tells us that our existence is but a brief crack of light between two eternities of darkness." So now do I grip the rails of my father's bed and tip him out of light, or do I lean in, and when the stubble of his beard grazes my cheek, betray him with a kiss? ಹಃ

Tumor

John Kay

We visited the life you fled
for a bed on a Houston cancer

ward. Utter strangers, we slept
in your sheets, used your pillows,

drank coffee from your cups,
examined your college photos,

your choices of art, the books
on heaven. In a week, we were

floating in your skin, carrying
your keys. In the beginning,

we tried to leave everything as
it was—then it didn't matter.

&

The Button Collector

John Kay

I saw myself across a huge room,
surrounded by strangers, my skin

a pearlescent underbloom. I
was dead, and I felt no grief at

the thought of joining myself
—it had been tough being human.

The button collector moved among
us with a pearlescent pen knife,

linen sack full of Union buttons
slung over his shoulder, and when he

came upon me, it was as it should be,
—he put his ear to my heart.

∞

Before the Jacaranda Trees Bloom

Sequoia Nagamatsu

The steady stream of stale air coming from a malfunctioning nozzle above Atsuko's head makes her eyes dry and reddish during her first plane ride across the Atlantic. She thumbs through a guidebook of South Africa while picking at her girlfriend Hallie's uneaten peach cobbler. Atsuko can hardly believe that she is on this plane. At Berkeley, just a few months ago, such plans would have been unimaginable. But here she is and the small monitor on the seat in front of her indicates they will be landing at Tambo International Airport soon. The cabin is dark, most everyone sleeping or trying to, though one by one slowly stirring as the pressure builds up in their ears. People crack window shades, letting in beams of light, and peer at the earth below. She is surprised by the similarities between the skyline of Johannesburg and any large city in Japan or America—crystalline financial centers surrounded by cement apartment complexes. But as Atsuko lifts her window shade higher, the endless expanse of shadows that she had mistaken for geographical features transforms into thousands of corrugated, rusted tin roofs of the shantytowns enveloping the outskirts of the city. Low flames and smoke rise from some of the townships. Many passengers are peering at familiar territory, the rest at a strange, uncertain world they would soon find themselves in. Hallie squeezes Atsuko's hand and rests her chin on her shoulder.

"Welcome to South Africa," Hallie whispers.

Paved roads give way to clouds of dirt swept up by cars and the footsteps of running children as Atsuko and Hallie make their way to Mamelodi, a busy township outside Pretoria. Hallie's father, a doctor at Pretoria University, has secured them a summer job at the Mamelodi hospice, where Hallie and Atsuko will also be staying.

It is surprisingly cool outside, with regular gusts of wind planting the smell of ancient soil in the air. Atsuko studies Hallie's blonde curls, blown by the wind. They almost seem to do a frantic dance to the music on the radio like the ones they would do themselves at Berkeley to one-hit wonders of the eighties until they both fell into bed laughing, kissing. Atsuko can see that Hallie is in good spirits from the expression on her face. Atsuko calls it the "O face" and there are several levels of it. Hallie swears that she has only reached her full "O face" with Atsuko. The music on the radio is suddenly interrupted by a woman who reports another man has been beaten to death outside of Johannesburg. Atsuko's face grows hot and her eyes begin to dart like frightened houseflies.

"Is it the same where we're going?" Atsuko asks.

"Pretoria is different. There are rarely incidents like that in Mamelodi. But this isn't Berkeley you know." Hallie squeezes Atsuko's leg. "Don't worry, I won't let anything happen to you."

"Promise?"

"Promise."

Atsuko tries to remain open to the experience but now that she is here, she is unsure whether she made the right decision to follow Hallie home after graduation. "One final hurrah," Hallie had said, "before our big good-bye." But even though it seems her breakup with Hallie is inevitable, the last words of her parents still rattle inside her mind like tin pans during an earthquake. When she returned home to Tokyo for her last spring break, she confessed to her parents that she and Hallie were in love. She had grown tired of lying to them. "Dishonor" is the English translation for the word her mother spoke although this is still the wrong word for a generation that values the status quo above all else. Dinner was silent except for the sounds of wet soba noodles smacking against lips and the occasional ringing of cicadas in the garden. No other words were spoken that week to Atsuko although her mother still did laundry and cooked for three instead of two. Atsuko's father even dropped her off at the airport and reached into his wallet to give her some money for snacks, but there were no embraces, no kisses or tears as with other families and lovers huddled on the curbside.

Atsuko remembers how her mother had always given her a tray of sweet *mochi* to silently tell her that she was forgiven whenever she misbehaved as a child, and even when she had not majored in economics like they had wanted. She wonders if there is a tray of *mochi* waiting for her now in Japan but can only imagine an empty table. The part of Atsuko that makes her face warm and uncomfortable, that makes her chest tighten, tells her that this time will be different, that she will have to walk a certain path in order to return home.

The roads of Mamelodi are lined with cement houses, tin shacks, and for the lucky, government-built or church-built homes with hot, running water and their own kitchens. It has been an hour since Atsuko and Hallie left the airport and only minutes since they passed the Pretoria city center on the highway, but they now seem worlds away. Every surface is coated with the color of the earth. The hospice itself seems like an oasis, a Spanish monastery with a brightly colored, blood-orange roof, nestled between the town's administrative district at one end and a Ford Motor factory at the other.

Hallie tells her that Effie, a Zimbabwean woman who has lived in Mamelodi for years, is waiting for them outside the hospice. Effie is one of the caseworkers and Hallie has known her since Hallie was a teenager.

"Her husband died a few years ago. AIDS. He was from here, in Hattfield," Hallie continues. "When he found out he was positive, he tried to get treatment but outside pharmaceuticals were banned back then. The government wanted to find an African solution. There were some clinics near the border still treating under the table. Effie worked at one of them. That's how they met. He died a couple of years after he returned with her but she decided to stay and make a life here."

"Is she positive?" Atsuko asks hesitantly.

"Yes."

Atsuko's eyelids feel as if they are twitching as she looks at Effie's tall, too slender body, a vestige of her Japanese upbringing of keeping your thoughts to yourself but not really. How she wishes that Hallie never told her about Effie's history, as she touches her eyelids with her fingers to make sure they are still. She was taught in Japan that HIV is the problem of other countries, other kinds of people. Such things were not spoken of and although Atsuko knows better, a part of her cannot help feeling that she will be tainted somehow.

"*Maskati, Maswera-sei!*" Effie says, embracing Hallie. Atsuko stands aside, waiting for an introduction in English, which Hallie assured her all children learn in school.

"*Taswera,*" Hallie replies. "Effie, this is the friend I told you about."

"Nice to meet you. You have come a long way. How are you finding our town?" Effie asks Atsuko. Her words come out full and rich, as if every word were coated with honey.

"I'm still finding myself here," Atsuko replies, unsure of what to say, having just arrived from the airport and suddenly very aware of her small stature, flanked by Effie and Hallie.

For the rest of the afternoon, Effie tells Atsuko and Hallie about the family that has been assigned to them—outpatients who require regular visits. She says that they have been her case for some time but that some people no longer like the idea of a Zimbabwean woman helping them. Effie seems to say this matter-of-factly but Atsuko can see the lump going down Effie's throat as she says the words. Effie hands Atsuko and Hallie a couple of files and introduces them to the photos clipped inside. There is Nohle, a young mother losing a battle with AIDS; her son, Zenzele, an active, HIV-positive six-year-old boy, who has been treated since birth and remains healthy. And then after pausing for a moment, Effie goes on. There is Thabiso, Zenzele's uncle. "He is the reason why I cannot go there anymore," Effie explains. "It is people like him who have been attacking Zimbabweans, blaming us for their poor circumstances. You must be careful of him."

"Do you think he would hurt us?" Hallie asks.

Atsuko adjusts herself in her seat and digs her fingers into the undersides of her thighs.

"No, I don't think so. But he will try to scare you off. He takes Nohle's money that she needs for her son and spends it on alcohol and women. He thinks he can live off their suffering."

When they are finished, Effie shows Atsuko and Hallie to their quarters—a small makeshift suite behind one of the offices. At their parting, Effie reminds them, "There is never nothing to do even in what looks like a hopeless situation. Sitting and holding their hand is more than many have here. It is something."

That night, after making sure the last staff person has left, Atsuko and Hallie curl up in bed together and talk about the day ahead of them. Atsuko holds the picture of the little boy, Zenzele, in her hand, staring at his wide eyes, robbed of innocence at such an early age. Atsuko knows that Hallie still has trouble understanding why she is uncomfortable with such matters, why she simply cannot view things as Hallie does.

"I didn't grow up like you did. We never heard these words when I was a child," Atsuko says. "The idea of this boy growing up with HIV is unreal to me."

"But we had friends with HIV back at Berkeley. It's not like you don't know about it."

"That's different." Atsuko breathes in deeply, wanting to tell Hallie that those people were never her own friends but always Hallie's from her gay and lesbian student groups and volunteering activities. They always made Atsuko uncomfortable and they always happened to be wealthy and white, a far cry from what she would be seeing soon.

Atsuko can barely sleep. She thinks about what it will be like when she meets Zenzele and his mother in just a few hours and she feels sorry for

Effie and her situation. A part of Atsuko wants to believe she can feel her pain, not being accepted at home herself, but at the same time she knows that she can never really know what Effie feels, or anybody here for that matter. Atsuko begins to question how well she and her parents really know each other and if the decisions people make in life are clouded by masks tied onto their faces by loved ones. She feels Hallie's hands slowly traveling down her body and the increasing warmth of her face as Hallie's kisses become deeper. Countless voices and shadows swirl through her mind as her eyes slip in and out of focus, gazing at the imperfections of the stucco ceiling, and creating abstract silhouettes that vaguely look like people she used to know, her house in Japan. She slowly falls into a dreamlike bliss as the images keep coming— stranger, chaotic, and more beautiful than her waking eyes could imagine.

The house that Nohle and Zenzele live in looks like a typical townhouse one might find in any lower-middle-class neighborhood in America—simple but not entirely devoid of effort. It was built by Haven, a local Christian organization, and had been given to Nohle a year earlier. Before this house, they lived in a plain wooden shed that still sits in the front yard next to a rusted water pump. When Atsuko and Hallie arrive, they find Nohle laying in bed. Zenzele is still at school.

"*Ek het dors,*" Nohle cries out weakly.

"She needs water," Hallie says. Atsuko searches for a clean glass in the kitchen, fumbling through cabinets while her heart pounds against the walls of her chest. She returns with a child's cup, handing it to Nohle, Hallie's hands guiding her frail fingers. "*Praat u Engels?*"

"Yes," Nohle whispers, barely above the sound of a thought.

"When will your son be home?"

"Soon."

"Are you okay right now?"

"Okay—*dankie.*"

Atsuko stands in the corner of the musty room, watching over Hallie and Nohle. Last night, she had imagined countless scenarios in preparing for this moment. But looking over Nohle's emaciated body, more delicate than a carton of hollow eggshells, Atsuko is overwhelmed.

"Why don't you wait out front for Zenzele. Nohle needs to rest. I'll stay with her," Hallie says, turning around.

Atsuko waits in the front yard, looking out into the dusty neighborhood. The thought of a boy having to come home to a dying mother every day saddens her deeply. Streams of children walk pass, and she starts to look for Zenzele. Finally, she sees him. His clothes, no doubt donated or handed down, look wrong on him—too large, too mature or too childish, not belonging to him any more than Atsuko belongs in his front yard. He has an inquisitive face, his eyes getting wider as he approaches Atsuko, his lips parting just slightly. They stand there for a moment not saying a word, studying each other. Atsuko smiles at Zenzele and he smiles back.

In the weeks to follow, Zenzele is always at Atsuko's side. Somehow, in letting this little boy into her life, Atsuko also comes closer to Hallie in a way she never thought possible. She now understands a little more what drove Hallie to devote herself to those whose lives were made uncertain.

One day during one of their walks to the school swings, Atsuko waves a folding fan with pictures of cranes on it and Zenzele asks, "What's that?"

"It's something to keep you cool," Atsuko says, handing the fan to Zenzele.

"Where do you live?"

"I live with Hallie at the hospice."

"No, tell me where you live, live."

Atsuko thinks for a moment. "I live in Japan," she says. "Remember, it's a group of islands very far from here."

"Can you take me there one day?"

"Maybe."

"Do you like football?"

"I don't know much about it."

"Mama used to take me to watch the older kids play before she got sick again. Effie said she would take me to a Sundowns game but then she went away."

"Do you miss doing things with your mother?"

"Yes."

"Where is your father?"

"Mama said he ran away before I was born."

Atsuko bites her lip. "What about your uncle?"

"He made Effie go away," Zenzele says angrily. "He makes Mama cry."

"Where does your uncle live?"

"I don't know. He just comes." Zenzele climbs onto one of the swings and tries to push himself off, barely getting off the ground. Atsuko stands behind him and gently pushes him higher and higher as he kicks his legs back and forth. "Can I tell you a secret?"

"Sure."

"You promise not to tell."

"Promise."

"I have a hidden treasure chest. Uncle Thabiso doesn't know. It's just for Mama and me. I bury it."

"What's inside?"

Zenzele is silent. He shakes his head. "You won't leave if my uncle comes?"

"No, I won't leave," Atsuko says, not really sure.

On their days off, Hallie takes Atsuko sightseeing. Atsuko loves taking strolls in the zoo, admiring the well-kept gardens and the Jacaranda trees lining the pathways. Hallie tells her they bloom into an ocean of purple in the spring. Atsuko cannot help but think of home as she walks among these trees, imagining the cherry blossoms that bloom at her parents' house. She wonders what her parents are gazing upon at this moment and if they truly know how far she has traveled. She wonders if they have embarked on their own kind of journey and if she is as much in their thoughts as they are in hers. She knows that this trip is a temporary solution but hopes that something will come of it to guide her. The uncertainties and disagreements in Atsuko's mind and life make her wonder if this is what being a grown-up really is, and if change is possible if you really want it.

"Maybe you can come visit me in Japan after all of this," Atsuko says, one day as she and Hallie have their weekly sushi at Kung-Fu Kitchen. Hallie mixes wasabi into her tiny tray of soy sauce and sprinkles ginger slices onto her sashimi.

"Maybe." Hallie takes a bite of her tuna roll. "But I thought we agreed that this would be it, you know?"

"We can't keep in touch, visit each other once in a while?"

"No, but—" Hallie's eyes focus on the table. "It's difficult. It'll make things difficult. I mean, where do you see us going?"

Atsuko's eyes begin to burn.

"We have different lives," Hallie says. "We *will* have different lives. Can't we just enjoy our time here?"

Atsuko nods. "If that's what you want."

Hallie reaches for Atsuko's hand across the table and the two girls finish their meal in silence.

Keeping Effie's promise, Atsuko and Hallie take Zenzele to a Mamelodi Sundowns game. Zenzele cannot stay still in his seat and jumps up and down whenever a goal is made, regardless of the team. During slow parts of the game, Atsuko takes him for a walk through the stadium and he gives high

fives to nearly everyone they pass. Atsuko smiles, seeing him in such high
spirits. When Atsuko and Zenzele return to their seats, Hallie is waiting with a
Sundowns jersey for him—several sizes too large. Zenzele swims in it, feeling
its new, shiny material as he watches the rest of the game, his eyes glistening
with the dream of what it would be like to be one of the players. Hallie holds
on tight to Atsuko's hand and the two look at each other, knowing this will
be one of those moments that they will always remember.

On every first Monday of the month, the hospice gives Zenzele an envelope
with the grant money that helps pay for medicine and living expenses. He
always puts the money in a pot in his mother's bedroom, where she can
easily get to it. It doesn't surprise Atsuko how Zenzele has had to grow up
so fast at the age of six, taking on responsibilities most adults would find
burdensome. But one day, Atsuko notices Zenzele digging in back of the
house, uncovering a large Winnie the Pooh mesh bag which appears to be full
of money. She wonders if this is the treasure chest that Zenzele mentioned
and if Nohle knows what her son is doing. When she tells Hallie about it,
they decide not to say anything. After all, Hallie points out, it is money that
Thabiso cannot touch.

Over the following weeks, Nohle's condition worsens. Atsuko takes
Zenzele for longer walks while Hallie and the medical staff from the hospice
try to feed her and do anything they can for her pain. The money in the pot
has disappeared. All believe that Thabiso must have snuck into the house
when Nohle was sleeping and taken it. Atsuko and Hallie begin camping in the
front yard of the house so that Zenzele will not be alone with his sick mother
at night and to make sure Thabiso doesn't cause more trouble. At odd hours,
Zenzele often climbs into the tent with them, sandwiched between Hallie and
Atsuko, his two honorary sisters as he sometimes calls them. Atsuko rests her
chin on Zenzele's gentle swirl of hair and finds comfort in his breathing—at
first fast and uneven then gradually tapering to slow, calming movements.

As the three emerge from the tent one morning, they find Effie standing
near the front door. Zenzele dashes towards her with open arms. Atsuko
and Hallie notice the tears welling up in Effie's eyes. Without a word spoken,
Atsuko and Hallie know that Effie is returning to Zimbabwe. Effie kneels
and embraces Zenzele, her movements slow and uneasy as if she has just
woken from a terrible dream and whispers something in his ear.

"I cannot stay here anymore," Effie says, as if her throat were filled with
dirt. "These men, they have destroyed my house, everything I have." Hallie
offers to take Effie into her parents' home but Effie will not have it. "I don't

want to create trouble for your family. Anywhere I go here, I am not safe," she says, looking down again on Zenzele.

Hallie drives Effie down the road, past the hospice and as far north as she will allow her, letting Effie out in once barren wastelands now dotted with thousands of refugees forced to return to their motherland or points beyond. Atsuko comforts Zenzele. He is upset that Effie is going but does not understand that he may never see her again. They watch as neighbors and friends walk past the township limits, in the direction Effie had told Hallie to drive, and one by one see their silhouettes disappear on the horizon.

Nohle is soon transported to the Pretoria University hospital with the aid of Hallie's father, and Atsuko and Hallie move from the front yard into Nohle's room. The once dark and quiet nights have transformed into a deafening cacophony showered by an orange haze from the burning homes outside. The nights become sleepless, marked by long periods of lying in bed, trying to fight images of those things newspapers never write about. Zenzele's eyes grow heavy and his spirit begins to fade, only showing itself for a brief moment when his *sisters* take him to see his mother. Atsuko knows that anything she tries to do will be of little comfort to Zenzele at this time. She can no longer tell Zenzele that Effie will be all right and that his mother will come home soon. The stark reality of his childhood has managed to touch his once innocent heart. Atsuko tries not to think about what will become of Zenzele in this shattered world and once again feels helpless and lost.

Zenzele's screams startle the girls late one night. In the darkness, they rush to his room and see the silhouette of a man, his hands gripped tightly around Zenzele's shoulders. Zenzele is now silent with fear, tears streaming down his face like spider silk. The man turns around and steps closer toward Hallie and Atsuko, the smell of cheap whiskey following him.

"Where is it?" he says, his voice growling deep like a truck engine.

Atsuko's stomach jumps.

"Who are you?" Hallie says. "What do you want?"

"I am his uncle. Where is it?"

"We don't know what you're talking about," Hallie says with a slight trembling as Atsuko takes Zenzele into her arms. Thabiso's wide, white eyes glare at them in the darkness, almost seeming to glow like an animal's.

"My money. I know this little thief has been hiding it somewhere." He pulls a small tin flask from his front pocket and takes a sip.

"The money is for Nohle and Zenzele."

"It is for family. I am family am I not?" He looks at Zenzele, peeking from behind Atsuko. "Who will care for him when his mother dies?" Atsuko shudders at the thought and covers Zenzele's ears. "Who will feed him, make sure he goes to school?" Atsuko cannot bring herself to look at Thabiso directly but feels his eyes gazing on her, so close she can smell the sweat on his shirt. Suddenly, Thabiso makes way for the door stopping to shake Zenzele by the shoulders. "Wait until your mama dies," he says, now holding Zenzele's mouth with one hand like a piece of wood in a vise. "Then maybe you will talk to your uncle." Thabiso turns around before he disappears in the shadowy street. "This is a dangerous place for a young, white woman and her Asian friend to be heroes." As soon as they are sure he is gone, Hallie drives Atsuko and Zenzele to the hospice, Zenzele finally falling asleep from exhaustion during the short car ride.

Hallie glances back at Atsuko and Zenzele in the rearview mirror every now and then, barely saying a word. Atsuko can see guilt in Hallie's eyes and the uncertainty that she can no longer protect her from the dangers of the world she grew up in.

"Maybe you should think about looking at flights to Japan," Hallie says with a dry throat. Atsuko doesn't respond, not really hearing Hallie's words, trapped in the moment of holding Zenzele on the darkened road. After Atsuko tucks Zenzele in bed, she turns to see Hallie waiting for her in the hall.

"Your parents have been calling since you got here. They've been leaving messages with my folks," Hallie confesses. "I'm not ready to say goodbye yet. I want you here. But maybe with everything going on like tonight and with your parents, you shouldn't be."

Atsuko remains silent for a moment and looks at Hallie and she sees someone there standing against the wall whom she loves but who she knows, with all the truths of their respective lives, she cannot.

"He's our family now. I want to stay a little while longer," Atsuko says, brushing a finger over Zenzele's forehead.

Atsuko and Hallie return to the house to gather Zenzele's and his mother's belongings a few days later. The locks on the front door are broken and they don't need to push it open to know that Thabiso has turned over every piece of furniture and emptied every drawer looking for the money. As Atsuko steps over broken chairs and shattered glass, she sees Thabiso across the street staring at her through the kitchen window. She and Hallie quickly gather everything they think Zenzele and Nohle might want and put them into large garbage bags and leave. As Hallie pulls away from the house, Atsuko sees Thabiso running in the side view mirror every time she glances back, keeping his distance but somehow keeping up. It isn't far from the house to the hospice, but the road seems endless this day. At times, Atsuko wants to cry out for help but her already quiet voice is silent in Africa, where she knows nothing. She believes no one would help even if she screamed. How badly Atsuko wants her parents at this moment to protect her from the world.

Arriving at the hospice, Atsuko looks back again to see that Thabiso has disappeared. One of the staff is waiting by his jeep, his expression telling the girls that something has happened that they do not want to hear. Hallie speaks to him in Afrikaans as Atsuko waits, looking into her eyes, seeing that it is taking everything that Hallie has to keep from collapsing. Hallie turns back to Atsuko and just stands there for a moment and begins to sob.

"It happened an hour ago," Hallie says. "Zenzele was at the hospital."

Atsuko embraces Hallie tightly and nestles her now damp eyes into the folds of Hallie's blouse. "What's going to happen to Zenzele? Are we going to pick him up?"

"No, he's gone," Hallie cries. Atsuko can barely understand her.

"What do you mean he's gone?"

"After seeing his mother's body, he ran away."

The entire hospital is searched, every closet and cabinet where he could have hidden. Some of the hospital staff, Hallie, her parents, and Atsuko drive the streets of Pretoria until it is dark and they cannot see past their headlights. They search again the next day and the day after that, walking through even the narrowest of alleyways in all the surrounding townships with a picture of Zenzele. But there is no sign of the boy that Atsuko and Hallie have come to call their brother. The two girls, now under the watchful eyes of two of the male hospice staff, sleep at Zenzele's house, believing he might return. But after two weeks of waiting, of worrying, there is no sign he is coming back. There is only a hole in the backyard where Atsuko saw Zenzele burying a bag of money. Atsuko hopes that it was Zenzele who took it and not his uncle. But there is little comfort picturing a lone boy in Africa, carrying so much money.

In the week before the Jacaranda trees usually bloom, nearly a month after Zenzele's disappearance, Hallie drives Atsuko to the airport. The turmoil of the country has become too dangerous for her. But Atsuko does not have to witness the sea of purple flowers to know that Africa is capable of beauty as well. Atsuko holds onto a picture of Zenzele in her purse and wonders where he is at this moment, hoping that he is all right but knowing at the same time that he isn't and will never be. A secret part of her will remain in Africa forever, she knows. It is this secret part, which she believes all people carry their entire lives, that make them who they are despite the paths they have chosen. It is the part that people look back on to remember what really matters. Atsuko and Hallie kiss goodbye and promise to keep in touch. Both of them know that in time this promise will be broken as their countries and their lives—the life their parents want for each of them—come between them.

As her plane begins its descent into Tokyo, Atsuko looks at the picture of Zenzele again, and holds his face to her heart. She looks out the window into her life, past the neon lights and the millions of people in their suits, and breathes in deeply as the plane touches down on the runway. ∾

Letter in Autumn

Wendy Wisner

I want you as I wanted your father,
years ago, in late afternoon. Outside,
rush hour, people sloshing through rain—
he and I at his mother's table, a bowl
of red apples and autumn's white hush.
Rescue me now, I thought, and I saw his arms
bound around me like gnarled branches,
the red apples shaking off his body. I knew
we were children, our bodies half ripe,
but I wanted him the way I want you now,
milk leaking out of me, sticky as tree sap.
The midwives say three more months,
but why wait, I can feel you
breathing on your own.

છ

Martin, 1918

Karina Borowicz

When life was meted out
he was allowed childhood
transparent enough to be seen through
from beginning to end.
He did not of course know
about the epidemic standing sentinel
at the border between twelve and thirteen.
Some games he played halfheartedly,
before bed now and then he'd refuse
his mother's embrace.
The last day of school
walking home on the dusty path
he dragged a stick
which drew a long line behind him.

℘

Shark Eyes

Christopher Schacht

He didn't hug her or kiss her or ask how was your day. He came in, sat down, and started talking.

There was this woman today. She came in about twenty weeks pregnant, been in a car accident. She was in bad shape. Her legs and her collarbone were broken, fractures in her skull, organ damage, and the fetuses, there was too much trauma in the womb. We didn't know if the mother was going to make it. She had an antepartum hemorrhage and went into premature labor. She miscarried about as soon as she arrived, twins, each one fit in the palm of my hand, they were so small, and we set them in the isolette. Little, tiny, dark brown things that squirmed, and they just looked cold. They were the smallest babies I've ever seen. We kept them alive for nineteen minutes. Nineteen minutes. They died, but I think the mother is going to live. Robert was the nurse on duty; you can imagine what he was like. He was so excited about the time, nineteen minutes, it was a new record in the state for fetuses at that stage, and especially rare considering how small our hospital is, and he thought maybe next time we could get half an hour or an hour or keep them alive and they'd develop into adulthood. But I couldn't even listen to him. He kept talking and I nodded and stared at his shirt and finally just walked away. I said I needed the bathroom. It's just ridiculous. Keep them alive? You can't keep them alive, they're twenty weeks. I don't know. I know it's possible, it just doesn't seem… like it can happen. At this one point, I don't remember when it was, toward the end, they opened their eyes. At about the same time. They opened their eyes. That never happens. Their eyes don't even work yet. They're just there because that's the plan. But the babies were laying in the isolette, their eyes open. It was… not right. I hate to say it, but I can't help it, looking at them, it reminded me of that time we went shark fishing in Florida, with Evan and his cousin. You get that shark out of the water, and once it stops thrashing around it just lays there, trying to breathe and moving a flipper or its tail just a little bit, it looks so much like it's dying, but you look into those eyes. There's nothing there. No life. It's like it was never alive. They're just black, dead eyes. And those fetuses, those things looked like they might be alive, but they weren't. They were just wriggling around, like a fish dying, or a worm dying, or like some ugly electric toy, losing power. Or winding down. Something about mimicking life without actually having it was revolting. It's like I told you in Florida, with the shark. I didn't feel sorry for it, I didn't pity it or even want to let it go. I just wanted it to die. I just wanted it to stop pretending to be alive. Of course we did everything we could, but Christ, they were twenty weeks. What can you do? Their lungs aren't even… I don't know, maybe I shouldn't be doing this anymore. I just don't want nineteen minutes. I don't want it to be like that. I don't want to celebrate nineteen minutes. I don't even want to see it. ଓ

Defect

Joanna Pearson

Lolling a glossy head that's way too fat,
the infant sags like pudding. His crossed stare
seems alien and flat. The MRI
shows river rock, a polished stone, the smooth,
unspeaking contours of a cool, white egg.
Tracing hieroglyphs, coarse cavern scrawl,

the mute encephalograph purls out its line,
an undulating strand of ink that reads
lichen, meal worm, toad stool, jade-green moss,
crouched fiddlehead. The baby doesn't blink.
Limp arms, un-kicking feet—he can't translate
to movement. Puddle-black, his eyes are blank.

His wealthy family from the Middle East
glides, dark-eyed, glittering, with scarves and servants.
With translators, a maid, and gilt tea service,
they mutely offer hot cups to the doctors,
tired teams of residents, and medical students.
Veiled, bowing, faceless strangers pass us sweets
of papery phyllo dough, chopped nuts, and honey.
Apologetically we take it, knowing
no one can do anything, there's nothing—
but then the mother speaks. She's lovely, young,
and gestures to her breasts. The lustrous folds
of fabric shift, revealing tears of milk.

A man translates, "She says he understands it
when she feeds him, that he gazes in her face
and sees her." We nod silently, well knowing
the baby's blind. When seizures lightning through
his heavy, milk-fed body, he contorts,
and crying, she beats a fist against her temple.

Our brains, behind their sutured calcium,
are trenched with secrets. Vermiculated whispers
go crackling through those wet, electric forests.
And yet within the gray-white convolutions,
our eloquence of furrow, groove, it's simple—
the answer we articulate is silence.

⁎

She Might Die

Magda Montiel Davis

She might die, my mother. If she dies, I'll come home from school in the middle of the day and she won't be here. No one will be here. Just my sister and she's busy being José Matos' yes-yes-yes girlfriend. And I'll do what I want. Because there won't be anyone here.

If she dies, I'll be like the bad American girls at Miami Elementary, who smoke and wear Thom McAn shoes with no socks, like Peggy Kirkpatrick, who has no mother and has this neat little mystery about her.

She might die, my mother, but aren't we lucky. That's what we are told. Lucky she has a strange disease and not regular cancer. Now that we are in the U.S.—*exiliados*, from Cuba—no money means no medical insurance and no medical insurance means no medical care. So we are lucky she does not have cancer because cancer is not strange—just deadly—and if she had cancer, she would get no medical care. But a nice research hospital has taken on my mother's strange case, her strange symptoms, her entire strangeness. Good teaching and research material, my mother.

No money for Catholic school, or a Brownie-Scouts uniform or even a Barbie doll. No money for medical care but she diseased strangely and so this tumor will be watched, studied, and even taken care of along the way. And aren't we lucky. Her lips, her cheeks, her jaw grew, swelled bigger and bigger, a balloon about to burst, a bomb on the verge. But her eyes shrunk, tiny yellow-brown eyes lost in her ballooned, bomb-like face.

Her feet, like elephant feet, and her hands. Oh my God, her hands—fingers, thick and browned and useless, nails ugly shards encrusted onto the nail bed, like broken glass. After an explosion.

I don't remember saying good-bye to my mother, not when she was carted off to the hospital. Or maybe she walked into the hospital herself. Drove there, probably. I don't remember, not the way my father remembers saying good-bye to his mother. A mother he never knew, a grandmother I never knew, waving silent to him, lifted limp into the white ambulance.

I only visit my mother once at the teaching and research hospital. My dad takes me. Jackson Memorial. A small table is next to her, yellowy white and metal and cold. I imagine Hemingway's Catherine sailing past yellowy-white hospital tables, Catherine in her white nurse's uniform loved by the wounded soldier, Catherine in her white starched headdress with pointed wings like the nuns at *El Sagrado Corazón* in my Catholic schooldays in Havana.

Hemingway was the greatest writer who ever lived. That is the opening line of my English paper for Mrs. Rosenwasser's sixth-grade class at Miami Elementary. Mrs. Rosenwasser doesn't start off believing in me but then she does. Maybe it's *Hemingway must have been a great man and in* A Farewell to Arms *he shows us that greatness.* I don't remember what I write exactly, but I try hard to come up with something different than the other sixth-graders. I get my A and Mrs. Rosenwasser believes in me.

Then Catherine, on her way to death's door, no longer sailed past yellowy-white tables and wounded soldiers. The yellowy-white table now lay next to her and still she said *Darling. Darling,* she called her wounded soldier. Beautiful words on her way to death, and her wounded soldier on his way out to the falling rain.

My mother says someone—maybe a nurse, maybe a cleaning lady—came into her hospital room in the middle of the night and opened the drawer of her yellowy-white table and stole something, I don't remember what. She heard and saw it with her tiny eyes, now colorless, now lost in her *on-the-verge-about-to-explode* swelled-up bomb-face. Someone stole something that was my mother's.

My mother has two blue-purple dots now over the top of her ears where patches of hair are missing. She sees me looking at the twin purple dots and touches the sides of her face and says *"Terapia."* Therapy, that's all she says.

Surgery, Dr. Katims says. Robert B. Katims, MD, the soft-spoken doctor who leans over her and smiles sadly. "Yes," Dr. Katims says. "The head will be split open. To burst the tumor, in your pituitary gland, the head will be split open, and then the tumor will pop." He touches her face. "Like a balloon."

"I have two daughters," is all my mother says.

So she comes home, my mother with her elephant hands and her purple dots and no surgery.

We ride to the *botánica* in Little Havana for her cure: a supply of ceramic roosters and Afro-Cuban rag dolls and that gooey *corojo* paste she puts on the bottom of our shoes and all her other *brujería* abracadabras and then on to the mechanic's auto shop in the air-conditioning-less car. She won't leave my sister and me alone in the house. We have no choice but to be dragged along. *"¿Las niñas, solas? No."* For the first time, she stands up to my father when we appeal to him to make out a case for us: We are fine, old enough, to be left alone.

She drives, slowly, carefully—by now, she had lost sight in her left eye. I sag hot against the window. I eat something sweet. A Three Musketeers maybe.

She says, *"Ay, Bebi, dame un poquito."* A little bit, she wants a little bit.

I break off a little bit of my something sweet, put it near her mouth and when her lips are at my fingers, I pull back. Like the shock of the turntable on the Hi-Fi—don't touch the needle barefoot especially if on a terrazzo floor, especially with wet hands. Or the burn of the just-percolated drops of Cuban coffee spilling on my fingers as I pull the *cafetera* off the stove. Quickly now, I pull back.

My mother's mouth tightens closed again. *"Te doy asco,"* is all she says. I disgust you. Not a chastising *A mother should not disgust a daughter,* but an affirmation of disgust of a daughter, for her mother.

Once she said, "For hours, they would have me sit in a big chair that zoomed up, down, went round and round." For hours she sat in silence in a tiny space behind a curtain and a team of medical students, then two, then three, then Dr. Katims would point at her elephant feet and sightless eye and her hands and her mouth and her hair. Her once-liquid black hair was now wild about her, not like I imagined Catherine's beautiful hair pin-curled under her nurse's cap then flowing behind her, beautiful in death even. Not like Ché's or Camilo's or Fidel's hair, waving high from olive-green tanks in those days of long ago in Havana. No, my mom's hair was now like I imagined Rochester's mad wife would have—*Jane Eyre's* Rochester—the wild, useless woman locked in that third-floor attic.

Dad breaks down and hires a *cantina* to deliver our dinner every night. The frozen TV dinners—meat loaf, green peas, peach cobbler—are fun at first. For a whole month, they are fun. And for the second month, not so much fun. And for this third month, even though *Mami* is home now, a *cantina.* But aren't we lucky? The *cantina* is owned by other *exiliados* and we get to pick: fried *bistec* with chopped onions and parsley—of course with chopped onions and parsley; how else are Cuban beef steaks eaten?—chicken fricassee, *masas de puerco*—messy, greasy chunks of pork. Smashed and then re-smashed green plantains. *Platanitos verdes.* Or fried sweet and ripe and mushy. *Platanitos maduros.* Desserts of *flans* or *arroz con leche.* Sweet egg custard, or soupy, milky rice pudding, cinnamon powder sprinkled prettily on top, the way *Mami* used to make it, almost.

It rains hard on the *cantina* man. Through the dusty screened window of our $100-a-month duplex, I see him. Through the beam of his car's headlights, I see him, the rain hard on him, the man turning our cardboard box of food this way and that, checking if he has the right order, the right plaintains—*verdes* or *maduros*, the right people. And my mom behind me says, *"Pobrecito."* Poor man. And I, along with my mother, feel sorry for him.

My dad, once the boss at the *béisbol* stadium for the Cuban Sugar Kings, now the bank janitor in Miami, tells his boss about my mom's sickness. The boss asks my dad if he has life insurance on my mom, and my mom says, *"Qué cosa, éste país."* What a country. Being practical about death. And not just that, when someone dies, she says, everyone eats. They get together and eat. And the dead are buried below the earth, not in pretty white marble boxes above ground facing the sun, like in Havana's *Cementerio Colon* with the Virgin Mary and statues of angels sporting giant, bird-like wings that look as if any minute could take off in flight.

But I understand death. Death and rain and Catherine. I do. There is "Leader of the Pack" and Bobby Goldsboro's "Honey" on Rick Shaw's Top 56 Hit Parade, and those songs are of death. Death and love lost. And James Dean and Buddy Holly and Roy Orbison and Ritchie Valens, didn't all of them die? Died young and in accidents. Car, planes. That is romantic, isn't it? Like Catherine. And she might die, my mother. ɞ

Describe a morning
you woke without fear.

Jacqueline Jones LaMon

It is four in the darkness and you cannot breathe.
You cannot will your chest to expand, and suddenly,
this is all right. You grope for the language of internal
surrender. Everyday, you have a choice, this choice.

Your left hand memorizes the grooves and nicks
in your mother's headboard. The textured flaws
keep you holding on and sane. You are used to living
on the memories of breath in your body, savoring

history. And so, your routine—two handfuls
of hospital visits each month—trips for breath in Brooklyn
when you are close to the unconscious edge. You race
for adrenaline to turn your heaves into tremors, to let

your fingers trace the oxygen that patterns your plastic tent.
And when you sleep, you are a fish, tired of her flop, too spent
to extract the valuable from the extraneous, another waterless day.
This day, your eyes focus on your mother's bedside table,

her only good watch, stopped. Your pale green canister of Isuprel,
empty for weeks—your Tedrol tablets, expired—your mind, alive
and dancing. When the voice of stars beckons, you follow, inside out.
You see your mouth. You touch your lungs. Your breath is incandescent.

∞

Hickies

Amy Kitchell-Leighty

The man at the grocery store thought the mark left by the portline
in Mollie's neck was a hickie which pissed her off but reminded me
of the hickie she did get in high school, the one she kept covered

with make-up and turned up collars and one morning, forgetting,
went to the kitchen to make toast, her hair up in hot rollers. For that
mistake, she was grounded a week. My mistake came at seventeen.

I wore a turtleneck in August, explained to my mother that hickies
were not made during some wild orgy-fest. I had gotten mine
from Matt who was just a friend and we were wrestling around

when he held me down and sucked on my neck. But she said
it didn't matter how I got it, it was trashy and that brings me back
to what I was saying before about my sister Mollie and that strange

man who laughed, then winked, then pointed at the mark
on the left side of her neck and said, *You've been havin' a good time.*
But blood had not been sucked to the surface of her skin in the back seat

of a car; instead, her neck had become an entrance for chemo
to be pushed into her body. To her, that mark was a stamp, an imprint
of a time in her life when isolation, vomiting, rosary beads, and hair loss

were as common as perking coffee. She'd had portlines in her chest,
in her neck, and once in her breast. The line in her breast was the most
invasive though the doctor waved his hand about, said *it doesn't matter*

where it is. She wanted the family, the dog, the dinner at six, but she wanted
to subtract the bone marrow tests, the constant fevers, the wigs.
If she could've gone back to that day, back to that grocery store—

if she could've bumped her cart against that winking stranger standing
in front of the deli, she would've told him is *was* a hickie and she *had* been
havin' fun. She would've winked back.

૪૦

To The River

Kelly Flanigan

I walk into Scott's kitchen, sweaty from basketball and needing something cold to drink, and there's his mom in just her underwear. Mrs. Labor's back has shallow rolls like fish gills and my eyes zero in on a raised diamond of flesh right above the elastic band. She turns and I end up looking at the top part of her crotch where dark hair pokes out.

"Joey, shit." She grabs a dishtowel from the sink and covers her chest.

I hold up my glass, words echoing in my brain: *I wanted some lemonade.* "Lemonade," I say.

"It's gone." Then she's gone. A door slams and I stand with my empty glass, my mouth open.

Scott opens the screen door and walks past me to the fridge. "Hey, did ya have to squeeze the lemons? What the fuck, man?"

"Your mom," I say.

"What about her?"

I saw her freakin' cans. "She said it was gone."

Scott rolls his eyes. "She doesn't know shit. Here." He reaches into the refrigerator and shoves a purple glass pitcher at me. "Smell it first."

We guzzle the lemonade then we're back outside and on our way to the river. Normally Scott would be the first person I'd tell if I saw some hot piece completely naked, but moms are touchy. I'd probably hit Scott if he told me he saw my mom without her clothes on. Besides, today is different. We haven't seen each other in six months, since his dad shot himself and Scott got sent away to the state hospital.

We sit on a ledge overlooking the river, throwing rocks and watching carp scatter. Everything's business as usual, like he was never gone.

"We should buy fireworks for the Fourth of July. That's, like, next week," he says. "Big ones. Set them off here. That'd be sweet."

"Are you even gonna be allowed to hang out?"

"I think so. Just with you probably. Mom's being really weird since I got back."

"But you're cool, right?"

He leans over the side of the ledge and spits into the water. "Check it out, man, they think it's food." The carp dab and nip at the white glob of Scott's spit.

"Did they really shock you?" I had heard kids talking at school about terrible things they do to people at those places. I'd seen shock treatments in movies and it looked like that could really mess a person up.

"I had to talk to this one lady a lot, my therapist," he says. "She was all right. Then I had to be in group, where a bunch of us sat around and talked about shit."

Everyone at school said Scott's mom came home from the store with the rolls she had forgotten for Christmas dinner and almost ran Scott over. He was standing in the middle of the street with blood all over himself. He had been woken up by a noise, they said, and had gone looking for his dad. He said he checked his parents' bedroom, then his dad's office. He walked by the bathroom and saw blood-spattered walls. Then, he said, he didn't remember anything.

"Some kids said that you tried to…"

Scott looks at me and I feel my face get hot.

"I mean, you know." It's my duty to tell Scott what people are saying about him. I throw a large stone, watch dark shadows in the water slide away.

"What, that I tried to cut my cock off?" He laughs and rockets a stone into the river like a football. "Jesus Christ. Do you believe everything you hear?"

"Did you?" I don't mean to ask this out loud, and he turns to me, another rock in his hand, and for a second I think he might throw it at me.

"Why the fuck"—he curves his hand and flings the rock backward toward the water—"would I do that to such a majestic monument?" He snickers and thrusts his hips.

"People said there was blood." I pause, look down at my own jeans. "There."

Scott stares straight ahead. I see the line of his jaw tighten and relax.

"Piss," he says. "I pissed my fucking pants, okay?"

I know my face changes even though I don't speak. Such weakness is outside of anything I can imagine from him. I think back to that day and imagine him standing in the street, his father's blood mixing with the urine on his jeans, and I wonder if that's when his head separated. If that's when, as my mom says, he went crazy.

"You really don't remember seeing him?"

He shrugs. "Would you?"

I don't have an answer. I don't really know what he saw. I wasn't allowed to go to the funeral; Mom said she didn't want me exposed to death. I tried to explain I was old enough—a teenager, finally—but she wouldn't listen.

"I don't know," I say.

I think about this while we walk home, our feet shuffling on the gravel, the dust turning our shoes a light brown.

In front of his driveway Scott stops and turns towards me.

"Don't tell anyone, okay?" He pushes his hands deep into his pockets and turns away from me.

By the time I get home the sky is more dark than light and I know I'm going to be in trouble. Mom didn't like Scott before he left. She didn't like Mr. or Mrs. Labor, his parents, either, even though Mr. Labor and Dad used to be friends. Mr. Labor was a photographer, and Dad repairs cameras. They worked together sometimes in our garage where Dad has an area set up so the mess stays in the garage and not in the house.

I walk up the driveway, and as I reach the screen door I hear my parents arguing from the kitchen, their voices amplified in the night air.

"I won't have him in my house!" Mom sounds like she's had too much coffee, her voice explosive and high. I hear dishes clattering against each other.

"How do you plan to explain that to Joe?"

"I don't need to explain anything. When did you decide that our child runs this household?"

"When did you turn into such a bitch?"

Silence carries out to the porch like fog and I hold my breath. I've never heard Dad swear at Mom before. When she responds, what feels like five minutes later, her voice is so low I can barely understand her. I imagine her standing inches away from Dad, her arms crossed over her chest.

"You call me whatever you want, that child is insane."

Scott. And she's wrong about him.

"He's having a hard time, Susan. He lost his dad, who was our friend. And a good man." Dad's voice rises and each word is punctuated with grief. "And he raised a good son. Scott *needs* Joey right now."

"Mom," I say, walking through the entryway into the kitchen, "he's not crazy. He's totally fine."

"You," she turns to me, a dish towel in one hand, "will not bring him into this house, understand?" Her eyes are animal, frightening but wide like if I moved at her she'd turn and run.

"He's my best friend!"

"Not anymore."

"Dad?" I look at his face and know how the conversation will end. He looks from me to my mother, then shakes his head.

"Listen to your mother, Joe." Exhaustion has replaced emotion. He turns and walks out to the garage. Mom and I stand in the kitchen, enemies, staring at each other.

"Bitch." I say this word all the time at school, and Mom has said it to me when I complain about chores, *bitch, bitch, bitch*, but here it's a weight, a foreign group of sounds that trips my tongue. Her lips press together and whiten, nearly disappearing. Her back straightens, ready for challenge. I take a step backward. She hurls the towel into the sink and leaves the kitchen. The screen door slams and she is gone.

It was the only thing I could think of to say. I'll pay for it for weeks, maybe months. I know the next time we fight she'll say, *well it's too bad I'm such a* bitch, *isn't it?*, emphasizing it. There will be comments to Dad, to friends that come over. *I'm a* bitch, *did you know that? Just ask Joey.* The word will become ugly and I'll probably never use it again. But I'll think it, and when I do, she'll be the first thing that comes into my mind.

I walk out to the garage and Dad hands me a Nikon SLR. When I help him work, which I don't do as often as I should, it's my job to break the cameras—bend something in one spot, pull a part out of another—without him seeing. That way he can continue repairing the same set of cameras and Mom won't bug him about money.

"Sorry you had to hear that, Joey."

I turn and bend the film catch on the Nikon. "It doesn't matter," I say.

"Does Scott talk about his dad?"

"Not really. We just talked about…stuff." I remember Scott's plea that I not tell anyone about him pissing himself.

"What did you do?" He is hunched over a pile of miscellaneous camera parts, picking through them with his index finger.

"We went to the river, same old thing."

"You do need to be careful with Scott." He glances up at me. "Your mother is right about that."

"I think he's fine."

"People thought his dad was fine too, Son. Sometimes people don't feel how they look."

I sit on a stool by the workbench. "Yeah, I guess."

"It's hard to lose someone. I can't tell you how much I think about him and how many times I've thought of all the times he sat right where you're sitting now," he nods at the stool, "and I tell you, I miss him here more than anywhere else."

"Was he your best friend?"

Dad nods and clears his throat, blinking a shimmer from his eyes. "Yeah. He was."

I go over to Scott's house the next day, leaving quietly through the kitchen so I can avoid Mom. Mrs. Labor answers the door. She looks like she's been crying, all red and puffed up. She's barefoot and has on jeans and a flannel shirt that's way too big for her. Mr. Labor's. It's open at the top and I see her bra. I move my eyes to hers, but I feel my face turning red.

"Scott's at an appointment," she says, rubbing her arms as if she's cold. "Do you want to come in?" She holds the door open, and I look past her into the living room. "I just made a sandwich. I'll make you one too and you can keep me company."

I stay because I want to, and because I know it'll piss my mom off. We carry our lunch outside and sit on the porch swing, and I watch her feet as I chew. They don't have any of the weird bumps my mom's feet have. And her toenails are painted bright orange.

"I'm glad you came over. I want to apologize for yesterday." She pauses. "In the kitchen." She looks at me like she's hoping I forgot walking in on her, seeing her.

I don't know what to say, so I just say that it's okay.

She tilts her head and smiles, but it's the saddest smile I've ever seen. I didn't know her very well before Mr. Labor died. She would appear with snacks for Scott and me, but she wasn't around a lot. I wish now that I could have talked to her more, before.

"It must have been a shock." She makes a sound in her throat that comes out her nose. "Appreciate your body now, how young and muscular you are. It won't last forever."

I want to tell her that it has lasted forever with her, that she's the most beautiful woman in the world, and I imagine her again—her underwear, the flabby parts of her back, her breasts—and I think about what it would be like to kiss her, there on the porch swing. What she would do.

"Has Scott talked to you about his dad?"

"He doesn't say much."

She takes a bite of her sandwich. I watch the bread compress under the pressure of her lips. "I thought that he might have. Since you're such good friends."

I shrug.

"Do you know any other boys your age that have lost their dads?"

I shake my head. Scott is the only one.

Mrs. Labor doesn't say anything else and the silence becomes true silence, not just a pause. I search for something to say. "We want fireworks for the Fourth of July."

"Oh, that's coming up, isn't it? I lose track." The flush that lit up her chest when I saw her naked appears again, slowly bleeding up her neck and into her cheeks. "Are you finished?" She stands, reaching for my plate, and, when I hold it out, her index finger, the nail painted with the same orange polish but chipped, brushes mine. I let go. She balances both plates and her glass; I reach out to help her, but as I stand the bottom plate slides like a door swinging open and slips from between her fingers. It hits the porch and shatters, covering my feet with small chunks of ceramic.

"Shit!" She hands me the other plate and the glass, drops to her knees and begins picking up the broken pieces, setting them on my plate. "I'm such a fucking klutz sometimes." She looks up at me, her light brown hair falling over one shoulder, and she looks for a second like she's my age, or close. "Sorry."

"It's okay," I say. "It's just a plate."

She sits down and leans against the porch swing. Her head in her hands, her shoulders start shaking and I can hear her gasping through her fingers.

I've never seen a grown-up cry like this. My first thought is to go home, to leave her there on the porch to comfort herself, but instead I reach out and touch her shoulder. Her long hair sticks to my sweaty fingertips, and I try to pat her and tell her it's okay, but the more my fingers move, the more tangled they get in her hair, so I kneel and put my arms around her.

She tilts her head and leans against me. I squeeze as hard as I dare. She smells fresh, like soap and light, and I close my eyes. Her arms are tight around my waist. I wonder what Scott would think if he came home and saw us like this.

"Joey." She pulls away, and turns towards me. "Thank you. I—" She pauses and her eyes get this real far away look in them, like she's left the porch in her head. "I needed that."

Mom is ironing when I get home. I sit on the couch and flip channels.

"Where have you been?" she asks.

"I had lunch with Mrs. Labor." I look right at her. "It was fun."

Mom opens her mouth then closes it again. She's as pissed as I knew she would be; her eyes flash. She retaliates. "The Morgans are coming here for the Fourth. We're watching fireworks at the river."

"I'm doing that with Scott."

"You'll have to tell him you have other plans." Steam hisses from the iron.

"What?"

"Joey, we've had this conversation. Your father and I think you need other friends. Not just Scott."

I turn the volume up on the TV.

"Turn that off. Go make a sandwich or something," she says, "then clean your room."

"A sandwich. Right."

I head to the kitchen. I don't want anything, but I take a plate from the cupboard. I stare at the plate, Mom's white china, and in my head I break it in two, right there in my hands.

"Joe! Come here." Her voice carries into the kitchen.

"Shit!" I yell and throw the plate onto the floor. It breaks into rounded triangular chunks, smaller chips crack off and scatter.

"What happened?" Mom runs into the kitchen and looks from me to the plate then back to me.

"It fell."

She stands with her hands on her hips and for the first time I see my mom has hips and a waist, although they're nothing like Mrs. Labor's. Mom is flat and straight up-and-down, like a boy.

Her face seems to close in on itself, her eyes squinting together and her mouth flattening out in a tight line. "Plates aren't free, you know. You can't just throw them because you're mad." She walks to the closet and gets a broom and dust pan. "Clean it up. Don't cut yourself."

"I didn't throw it." While I sweep up bits of the plate I remember Mrs. Labor, her arms around me, her smell. If I could do it again, I would kiss her. Not on the mouth, of course, but her ear. The lower part that meets her neck, the part that smells like light.

When I sit down to dinner that night my food is divided onto three paper towels: a slice of meatloaf on one, green beans on another, and a baked potato on the third. The juice from the green beans is soaking through and turning the white a pale green.

"What's this?" I ask.

Dad lowers the corner of his newspaper to look at me. "We don't break plates in this house. Not by accident, not on purpose." He flips the paper back up. "Eat your dinner."

I sit down and spread the meatloaf to the four corners of the paper towel, load the potato with butter and sour cream and then squash it to pieces. I save the green beans for last and by the time I'm done, rivulets of liquid bean are spreading across the table.

"What's the matter with you?" Mom puts her fork down and stares at me.

I give her the meanest stare I can. I feel like crying but I won't give her that. I want to say "you are!" and throw my food at her and tell her that if she's going to try to keep me from being friends with Scott then she's a bigger bitch than I thought.

"May I be excused, Dad?"

"Clean up the table, Joe. Then you can go to your room."

"Craig," Mom starts, looking at my father.

"Let him go. It's enough."

Two days later, Scott and I walk to the river. This time we're quiet. He stands over a cement drain with a look on his face I've never seen before. He leans into the drain and pulls out a paper bag. He holds it weird, like it's something that might break.

"Did you get fireworks?" I reach for the bag but he pulls it away. Before he left, Scott always had ways of getting us the coolest stuff, like pepper gum that would burn our tongues and rocks with crystals on the inside.

He keeps one hand under the bag, slides his other hand into it, and pulls out a small gun. He holds it up for me to see.

"Whoa," I breathe. "Where'd you get this?" I am stunned. I lick my dry lips; my tongue feels too big for my mouth. "Mom would kill me if she saw this!"

He sets it in my hand and I'm surprised by how heavy it is but light at the same time. I put my finger on the trigger, the pad of my fingertip spongy against the thin sliver of metal. I turn away from Scott and aim the gun at a tree, squinting my eye shut and sticking my tongue out of the corner of my mouth like I see on TV. I feel the gun from the tips of my fingers to my shoulder. I'm hyper all of a sudden, imagining us taking out birds, squirrels, even the carp in the water.

Scott steps closer and I lower the gun. He runs his finger up and down the barrel and looks at me.

"It's just like his. Just like the one he used."

And like invisible fingers are pressing on it, the gun gets heavier in my hand. My excitement is gone and I look at Scott. I hear the scratching of claws on bark as two squirrels chase each other up a tree behind me.

"Put it in your mouth," he says. Scott's face is pale and the black parts of his eyes are too big.

"What? Are you fucking nuts?"

"It's not loaded." His voice is mechanical. He's acting as if he's not even here.

"What are you talking about?" My throat feels like it has a baseball in it and I blink to keep my eyes clear. Scenes from horror movies flash through my head, people running away from killers. The thought that Scott has come to kill me stops everything and I get wobbly all over.

"Don't be a pussy. I need to see what it looks like."

He grabs my hand and raises the gun, turning the barrel towards my face. I want to resist but he moves too fast, and in a few seconds it's in my mouth and I can't move. My body is rigid now, frozen. The metal clicks against my teeth like cracking knuckles. I try to swallow but my teeth hit the top of the barrel and a thick gagging sound comes out instead. The sun seems to be brighter than I've ever seen it and sweat pours down the sides of my face. My heart pounds and every time it thumps I'm sure I'm going to puke.

"Scott," I start, but when I talk the barrel moves. I imagine the trigger moving a millimeter too far. I look toward the road, for cars, for a bicycle, anything.

"I bet he cried too." He's watching the ground, swaying a little like he's going to fall over. "Tell me what you're thinking about."

I don't know what he wants me to say.

He pulls the gun from my mouth, takes it from my hand. Our eyes connect and in that second I see that my mom is right: there's something wrong with my best friend. I feel sick. He puts the gun back under the drain and begins walking back home.

We are quiet walking. No words seem like the right ones. When we get to his house, he sits on the front steps. "You can go home. I'm just going to sit out here for a while."

"Do you want me to get your mom?"

He laughs. "Yeah, right."

"What are you going to do with…you know."

"I don't know." He looks at me. "Christ, Joey, I'm not going to do anything bad. You're worse than my fucking mom." He turns and gives the finger to the front door. "Bitch."

I get angry. "Dude, she's your mom!"

"Whatever, man." He leans back, resting his elbows on the top step, and closes his eyes.

I walk away, looking back over my shoulder until I can't see Scott anymore. His words don't match up with the look in his eyes at the river and my stomach feels like it's going to explode. I'm still sweating and as soon as I'm out of sight of Scott's house I sit down on the side of the road, afraid I'm going to throw up.

I feel the vibration of an approaching car and stand up quickly. It's a pickup, no one I know, but I wave anyway. I want to go back to the river, sit and think and watch the fish swim and throw rocks and pretend that today didn't happen. But the sun is getting lower and I don't want Mom more mad at me.

I smell dinner as soon as I walk in the door and realize that I'm starving. The melted cheese from the casserole begins to fill me before I can see it.

"Just in time," Dad says and hands me a cardboard picnic plate. I look at the dividers, slide my fingertips into the grooves and wonder briefly if the gun left any residue on my hands.

Mom talks about the Morgans, arriving tomorrow morning, and how they're going to the Black Hills after they leave our house. She's decided that we should take a family trip, the three of us. I drink my milk and listen to the remains of my summer time with Scott fade away.

After dinner Dad goes out to the garage to work on cameras. I follow him. "Can I try to fix one tonight?" I ask.

Dad seems pleased to see me. "Have a seat," he says, and slides his equipment over so I can watch him as he works. "You didn't say much at dinner."

"Do you miss Mr. Labor?"

Dad uses a tiny silver screwdriver to open the back of a Nikon. "I do, very much. Probably as much as you missed Scott when he left."

"Mom doesn't."

"She tries, Joe." He hands me a pencil flashlight. I turn it on and point it at the underside of the camera.

"I hate her sometimes." I whisper this, and not because I'm afraid she'll walk into the garage and hear. I look at Dad's face. The flashlight shadows his face, but I hear him sigh.

"I know you do." He turns the camera over and begins working on the lens.

I don't tell him that I wish Mrs. Labor was my mom. That I would never hate her no matter what she did.

"I'll be right back," I say, and stand up. Dad nods and hunches over the lens.

I open the door and stand halfway between the kitchen and the garage, watching Dad work alone, without his friend, and I see myself years from now without Scott, and wonder if Dad could have done anything to stop Mr. Labor from doing what he did. I wonder if it's possible to stop the past.

Dad and I work into the night, and by the time we go to bed I have fixed my first camera. I read *Shutterbug* and think about Mrs. Labor and how even though she isn't like the girls in the magazines Scott looks at, she's the prettiest woman I've ever seen. And when I fall asleep I see her face, her hair, in small shapes against the inside of my eyelids.

A noise wakes me and my first thought is that it's Scott, that he snuck into my room. My stomach starts to roll when I remember the gun and I open my eyes, trying to focus on the furniture in my room glowing in blue moonlight. I am cold and I realize that something is wrong. I am lying on my side, and my hip is wet and itchy. I squeeze my pajama bottoms and when I smell piss on my fingers I am wide awake.

Fuck. I push the blankets back and quickly take them and the sheets off of my bed. I sneak clean sheets from the hall closet. I press my ear against my parents' door and hear Dad snoring. I finish making the bed.

The sky is beginning to change from purple to blue; it's dawn.

I walk to the river.

I reach into the dark cement drain; the paper bag is still there. I lie down on the ledge. The stone is freezing on my damp pajamas and I shiver. I press my cheek into the grit of the ledge and know that it will leave marks that I won't be able to explain to Mom. There is so much that I will never be able to explain to her.

A carp splashes in the middle of the water and I begin to cry and because I'm alone there I let everything go and scream and shake until I'm sure I'll never stop. I pick up the bag, take out the gun and look at it and imagine where it's been, and I know that nothing with Scott will ever be the same.

Keeping my trembling fingers away from the trigger, I remove the clip. As I pull it out and see the bullet inside, a static sound rushes in my ears and I dig my fingertips into the soft ground. I take the bullet out and look at it—small, sharp. I put it in my pocket. I can't feel it, it's so light, and I look down to see if it shows through my pajamas. I press around it until a dark mark appears, but when I move my hand again the bullet disappears into the fabric.

I walk to the edge of the river and lean forward. Lean until I almost can't see the edge anymore, and I look down into the water. It's like the ocean, wide and big, the current swirling through.

I get dizzy. Black spots poke at my vision. One more centimeter, I think, and I'd be gone. I'd be in the river, floating, not struggling against the current but letting it pull me south. I throw the gun as hard as I can. I step back. ∞

Miguel Plans a Revolt

Ines P. Rivera Prosdocimi

Sometimes in the day the blinds crack open,
then I can see a sliver of the outside:
some sun   a palm tree's crown   cloud bits.
My wife is selling our family home.
If anything should happen to me, have
compassion. She thinks
I do not know, believing I've misplaced

my memories. I still see   Mama and the aunts
plaiting their wool hair, feel a spring push
against my back,   that old mattress we shared.
The upright piano whose teeth woke us
every morning, I cannot   escape
my head. I sit rocking. Brother, I wait,
know we are two fingers from the same hand. Come
see if I've pulled tufts of hair or dropped
my spoon like a baton on someone's head.

We need a new master-lock for the front gate;
tell no one   the combination. Plant
giant cacti with bold needles,   help me
out of this room,   it has been a long time
since someone touched my hand. At night -
       a low humming. I pat the songs we sang
on my lap, laugh a little to myself. Do you remember
where we hid candy? The Pilón coffee can.
It waits there with the letter I've written
to secure this birthright of ours. Brother, do not worry.
Our victory will be as brilliant as bite marks -
       those roses up and down my wife's arms.

੮੭

Ninety-seven

Paola Peroni

Dr. Benovitz's office is on the ground floor of the Majestic on the Upper West Side. The décor is antiquated, gloomy, and clean like the doctor himself. In the waiting area, two nurses sit behind a counter, disposing of paperwork and answering the phone. Two rows of four chairs face each other, with little space in between them, imposing an awkward intimacy in the cramped room.

Mrs. Berman sits on a chair with her wheelchair parked in front of her. Her body has withered with age, leaving her features exposed, almost skeletal. Sparse strings of discolored blond hair drop from her head amidst bald patches that no amount of combing can cover. Maria sits next to her on the edge of a chair, her plump body bulging from her clothes, her worn hands folded to hide bitten nails. Her uncertain eyes focus on the old woman.

"I have just turned ninety-seven, and everybody called me on my birthday. Imagine, my son phoned me all the way from the Philippines," says Mrs. Berman.

Maria can't imagine the Philippines. She couldn't even place it on a map, but it must be far, maybe as far as Guatemala is from New York, where she has spent half of her forty years. All she knows is she alone was with Mrs. Berman on the day of the woman's birthday, and the phone did not ring.

Another patient, a young woman, takes a magazine from the rack against the wall, but keeps it closed on her lap. An electric blue silk scarf matching her fine suit is wrapped around her head, and the deep-set gray eyes unadorned by eyebrows blaze on her pale complexion.

"It's hot in here. Open the door a little," says Mrs. Berman.

Maria gets up, opens the door, and leaves it ajar. She returns to her seat, and sneezes, covering her nose with one hand.

"You should wash your hands," says Mrs. Berman. "You don't want to pass on your germs. I always wash my hands, always."

Maria wipes her hand over her jeans.

"Most people say they are clean, but they are not," Mrs. Berman says with disdain. "They wash their vegetables in the sink where they have rinsed their hands and dirty dishes. Can you imagine that?"

Maria is about to bite her thumbnail, but stops herself in time. She remembers bathing her baby brothers in the kitchen sink at home.

"I wash my vegetables in a clean bowl. Always have," says Mrs. Berman. "You haven't been with me for long, but wait and see. I'll teach you everything."

Maria relaxes, and curls the hair around her ears.

"I'll even make you lose weight. You need to lose weight. Didn't the doctor tell you to lose weight?" asks Mrs. Berman.

Maria turns, and glances at the woman sitting across from them. The magazine is still closed on her lap, and the woman is looking at them.

"You don't need the doctor to tell you. I can tell you myself," says Mrs. Berman, undeterred.

Maria senses the burden in the woman's sunken eyes.

"The girl who was helping me before you lost nine pounds. I made her lose nine pounds. She's never been happier. Didn't I tell you about that girl?" asks Mrs. Berman.

Maria says hesitantly, "That was Carmen?"

"Nine pounds," repeats Mrs. Berman to underscore her achievement. "And you don't have to starve. You can eat as many vegetables as you want. And when you get hungry, eat an apple. Half an apple is even better. Save the rest for later."

Maria gazes at the woman across from them; their eyes meet and Maria shrugs, apologetic.

"But you eat ice cream. Don't think I haven't noticed," says Mrs. Berman, calling Maria back to order. "You'll never lose weight if you don't stop eating the ice cream I keep in the freezer."

Maria tugs her shirt down as far as it goes.

"Fat is bad for your heart. I had surgery, you know." Mrs. Berman opens one button of her shirt to reveal the scar on her wrinkled skin. "But I recovered. I am ninety-seven."

Maria does not know what to believe, but wants Mrs. Berman to believe she believes whatever she is saying.

"That's why you must lose weight. But you must lose it slowly. The fat is around your heart, and it's bad for you to lose it fast."

The woman sitting across from them gets up, and asks the nurse how much longer she will have to wait. The nurse tells her she is next, and the woman returns to her seat, grabs a new magazine, and clutches it to her chest as if to contain her irritation.

"I've outlived my sisters and my friends," says Mrs. Berman with a touch of sadness. "I don't know if it's a blessing or a curse."

"This is a lot to lose," says Maria, her discomfort tamped down by the change in Mrs. Berman's tone.

"It's not easy to be ninety-seven," says Mrs. Berman. "I have so much to say, and nobody left to listen."

"Nobody ever listened to me," whispers Maria.

"Maybe you don't want to live this long. I've lived too long," says Mrs. Berman.

Dr. Benovitz appears in the waiting room; blending with the décor he is almost invisible.

"Did I tell you I just turned ninety-seven?" says Mrs. Berman.

The woman in the waiting room gets up and confronts Mrs. Berman. "I feel you've been telling us since you were six. That's why you're ninety-seven, and some of us will never reach fifty." She yanks off her scarf, revealing her bald head and glares at Mrs. Berman.

"I don't like people talking in my face," says Mrs. Berman as the woman rushes inside the doctor's office.

Maria sees white dust carried by the breeze. She sees her mother collecting the sheets hanging out to dry, her face scarred by wrinkles from years of working in the sun.

"My mother was sixty when she died, but she looked ninety-seven," says Maria. ∂

My Father's Hands

P. Philip Cheung

The perfumed juices drip down his long, smooth arms bared by sleeves rolled up past his elbows. He distributes the four even slices to Mother, me, and my two sisters. His slender fingers slip and slide over the saffron hairy stone. He slurps off the remaining meat. This is how our family eats a mango in 1950s, 44 degrees north latitude Ontario. It's a family affair, unlike in Southeast Asia where I've seen individuals peel it like a banana, skin segments flopping like hand drapery. We share the sweetness of one fruit, carefully dissected by Father. That's his role in the family. Every week, he surreptitiously drops exotic foods into Mother's shopping cart. He has eclectic tastes, a carryover from his upbringing in the subtropical former British colony, Hong Kong. He chooses for his desire and nostalgia but also for our education and enjoyment. Smoked oysters, black Russian caviar, Melton Mowbray pork pie, smelly blue cheese, pickled rolled herring and Marmite, all make it to the breakfast table next to bland, tepid, scrambled eggs and doughy, white, sliced bread. Cautious, practical, Niagara Falls-born Mother puts up with these flights of fancy. Father is the explorer and magician. He's the one who gives unsolicited tips on how to enhance the flavours and textures of a dish. "It needs more ginger and orange peel. Grate the cheese finer. Stew the meat gently." These culinary sparks however, are never realized with his own hands, as they may be in other Chinese families. In contemporary mainland China the father is known to be the better chef but only performs for guests, while the mother is in charge of the drudgery of the daily routine. But in suburban Downsview our family rarely entertains at home and if we do, Mother is the self-effacing cook; smiling, modest hostess; gracious server; and grouchy, cleanup maid. So Father's hands are never tested as a cook. But it's Father who knows how to manipulate food from distant places. These shared hors d'oeuvres, snacks and relishes are all orchestrated by his discriminating hands. A gentle squeeze to the plump red, thin-skinned persimmon will ensure we avoid the anaesthetic tingle of the unripe flesh. It's his manicured fingertips that demonstrate how to fold back the leathery skin of a scarlet pomegranate, so that the teardrop seeds pop forward in a perfectly segmented mouthful. Applying expertise from years of medical training he scrupulously fingers each slice of smoky, kippered herring to extract every hidden bone, so we can delight in the savoury English breakfast without effort or apprehension.

One might say it was Father's hands that saved him when the Japanese occupied Hong Kong during World War II. As a medical student he had been practising at a Red Cross first aid station in North Point, on Hong Kong Island. The station was taken over by Japanese soldiers who set Father to washing dishes. It seems that he was so useless at this activity that the enemy gendarmes sent him home. Relatives laugh when recounting this story, implying that he was clumsy. But probably he was just too slow from lack of experience—the family housekeeper did the dishes—and overly methodical and meticulous. I can just imagine his elegant, gentle fingers fastidiously handling aluminium canteens and mess tins as if sterilizing O.R. instruments.

Father's hands, however, are not just careful and particular but also potentially imaginative. He was born the ninth of twelve children into a creative and musical family, though he was the only one who didn't receive piano and singing lessons as a youth. He excelled in school and was encouraged to concentrate on his academic studies; he was the first in his family to pursue university education. All the others worked in their family businesses: Hong Kong's first modern ice cream factory, their biscuit manufacturing empire and western restaurant chain.

Perhaps Father's manual activities have served as a break from too much cerebral endeavour. During both his career and retirement his dexterous, inspired hands are engaged in recreational activities: patching his own clothes, darning his son-in-law's socks, knitting a scarf for his "lady of leisure" wife, turning old socks into wrist warmers, fashioning a waist pouch from his daughters' discarded denim jeans, soldering burnt engravings into his sculpted balsa wood carvings, plastering flour and water papier mâché toy animals and buildings, moulding ceramic teabag caddies and dabbing at oil and watercolour cows and portraits.

Most enduring for me is the magic Father's hands impart on playtime during this era before ubiquitous TV. Like Pinocchio's Geppetto, he crafts toys from wood, using a single disposed spool, an ordinary rubber band and thin dowel. Wind it up and it twirls across the shiny surface of the freshly waxed and polished hardwood floor. Lying beside the fraying Persian carpet, I am carried away in an ancient palanquin to the caves and palaces of Aladdin. Stories of genies and magical lamps pop out of the big story book propped on Father's knee. After teeth are brushed and pyjamas pulled on, we sit curled up in his lap under the yellow glow of the antique brass lamp. Every evening these same tender hands turn the pages of faraway, long ago paradises, until bedtime yawns close the book once more. Then as ritual dictates, Father must carry each of the three elves across the icy floor by turn, to tuck into bed, because we have conveniently forgotten to wear our slippers. Then, clutching the maroon, woollen sock doll sewn by Father's patient hands, I hug the comforting placement of the crisp, white sheets, as Father and Mother bid me sweet dreams.

In his final years, the skin of Father's hands becomes a dark, burnished bronze hue, stretched over unbendable joints. I watch this fiercely independent man struggle to tie his own shoelaces and manipulate rubber-gripped cutlery in order to cut up soft custardy quiche into manageable bites. Still beautiful in shape and proportion, Father's hands are now prisoners of the whims of scleroderma. Now it's my turn to seek out exotic treats to bring to the breakfast table: fragrant durian toffees; salty salmon jerky; fermented, oozing natto beans. And it's my turn to create knitted stuffed toys for the grandchildren.

Until my father passed away, I never really noticed that I have engaged in a similar pastime of making handicrafts. In fact, I never even realized that *he* possessed this skill until I thought about what he had passed on to me. By the end his hands were like lifeless ice sculptures. Most of the objects created by them are no longer with us. The tenderness he applied, however, to a frayed, forgotten sock or the fragile skin of an over-ripe Chinese gooseberry, as he handed them to me transformed, will always endure. ∞

The Heart Long Gone

Maria Williams-Russell

The blood tests reveal my body is attacking itself -
"mistakenly," the doctors say. "There is no reason it should be alarmed."

"How long can a body live without its heart," I ask and
they act as if their clipboards had said the words.

"It's not your heart," my husband sighs in the car. But I keep
clutching my chest knowing breath is slipping, the heart long gone.

***

A milky pallor spreads over the mountains in Central America,
the major cause of bus accidents in the tropics.

In many cases, the fog is too sudden, the fall
too steep for rescue.

I remember the red orange tassels swinging, the shuffle
of the chickens, the noisy snore

of the woman beside me, before we were fast
into the opaque skirts of that ghost.

***

"It is a matter of place," I say, the New England forest
gathered by the road to witness my passing by.

"If home is where the heart is, where's the body?"
Neither my husband nor the trees reply.

***

Our bus veered toward the mountain, crashing
softly in the wet trees. Sightless, all

pulses and breath, we waited hours in the mist. I thought
of my own disappearance, the forced habit

of clouds. I will never know
if it was the woman beside me who placed

her hand silently over my heart
that day in that deep pool of fog

or if it was a manifestation of a ghost come
to give comfort so close to heavenly, I would

never speak of it, nor feel the rise of my chest
toward any other being completely again.

***

With hands between my knees, we turn effortlessly
into the driveway, the yellow aluminum siding glaring in the sun.

&

Air Hunger

Sandra Meek

What you hear, barely, the body's
last music: sword

of snow melt, stalagmites'

mineral drip. Struggle is what no longer
translates: her sleeping

mouth hung open, the way a snake

unhinges—

Do you remember milk
and vanilla spilled

to fresh snow, how something
so clean had to be so

quickly eaten? Before the food could drift

away from the body
of cold water too clouded to hold

even the face that mothered it
there, into this one

blue bowl.

&

Smart Enough

MaryLee McNeal

Ralph Peterson didn't retain many memories of childhood; in fact he managed to completely erase memory of a dozen trips to Denver to repair his lip and palate. Yet he remembered fully, in vivid detail, one family dinner when he was eight. It was a winter night in River Springs, Wyoming, 1959. He'd dropped his fork, then bumped his head on the table in the effort to retrieve it. He tried out a word he'd learned from a neighbor boy that day, except that when it erupted from Ralph's mouth, it came out "thit-ath," instead of *shit-ass.*

His older sister Mary's eyes widened in amusement; his parents both stared at him. "What did you say, son?" his mother asked. He wanted to sound powerful and reckless, the way his neighbor had, so he repeated, louder and with gusto, "*Thit-ath!*" At that his father burst out laughing. This was the crux of Ralph's memory—a vision of his father, head thrown back, roaring with laughter. And his mother's voice scolding, "Stop that! It's not funny. This is exactly the kind of thing that will bring more trouble on his head!" Ralph was confused, hurt by his father's laughter, and at the same time worried at his mother's tone.

But his father laughed even louder. "What? The school will kick him out of his second go-round in second grade for saying *thit-ath*? His life will be ruined?" Ralph's father continued laughing even when his wife hissed at him through tight lips, "Shut your mouth, you hyena!" This was the other part Ralph still remembered—the word *hyena* hanging over the table, his father gleefully sputtering, his mother glaring.

Even though it hurt, Ralph loved his father's laughter; there wasn't much of it in their house. The word became a joke between them when they worked together at the small table in the garage. His father was a dentist, and loved building small things with his hands. Ralph assisted, handing his father glue, nails, or small pieces of wood as they constructed bird houses, small wooden boxes, trivets of latticed wood pieces. "Say 'shit,'" his father would whisper, and Ralph practiced until he got the *sh*-sound almost right. It took months. The corners of his father's normally down-turned, disappointed mouth always shifted into a grin when he teased, "Say 'shit.'" They'd played that little game long after Ralph's speech had improved, played it until his father's death, in fact.

Eventually, the nuns at the Catholic grade school made it easy for Ralph to graduate, but high school was a greater challenge. After being called "harelip" and "dumbo" a few times, he learned to avoid his peers at River Springs High. He was protected by two or three kindly teachers, and his mother's sharp tongue kept the bullying at bay. Ralph became a sort of mascot/bat boy for the softball team. Teachers passed him on to the next grade, giving him credit for "effort."

Ralph had developed a lumbering gait as he grew taller, and his awkward body and narrow, odd face didn't improve with age. Adults who'd known him all his life found his slight speech impediment annoying, averted their eyes when they met him, and rarely said more than, "How's it going, Ralph?" without waiting for an answer. A final surgery, when he was a sophomore, brought scant improvement to his speech, but at least he was able to partially hide the scars with an uneven mustache. He already had a reputation in town for being "a bit retarded," but Ralph was smart enough to know that people thought he was stupid.

His father died of a heart attack when Ralph was sixteen. Mary came home from college in Denver for the funeral, but Ralph was the one their mother turned to for comfort. At his father's grave, his mother's face was pinched and sour when she spoke to Mary, or to the other mourners, but relaxed into a smile when she looked at Ralph. As they left the cemetery, she leaned so heavily against him that he was afraid he'd stumble. But he didn't; he was stronger than he thought, and proud of himself for not crying. "My boy," his mother muttered to the priests who prayed over her husband, "what I'd do without him, I don't know." She looked up adoringly at Ralph, who was already over six feet.

When Ralph finished high school—"by the skin of his teeth and *my* efforts," his mother said often—they visited Mary, who had graduated and was working in Denver. Ralph was unnerved by Mary's apartment building with its long halls and dozens of doors in a row, each exactly like Mary's. On the way back to River Springs, he told his mother that he couldn't wait to get out of Denver—too many look-alike doors in one building, too many tall buildings downtown.

"That's big-city living for you," his mother said as she steered their big Chevy over the Colorado border and into Wyoming. "I don't know how she stands it. You and me, we stick to the good old hometown, right?" She smiled at him the way he liked.

When they attended church each Sunday, she smiled the same way. After mass, as people stood talking outside on the steps, his mother spoke for him so he didn't have to struggle to be understood. If someone asked, "How are you today, Ralph?" she'd reply, "He's fine—has a job driving Freeman's van." If Father O'Farrell said, "You're looking well, Ralph," she'd say in a loud voice, looking toward Ralph as if he were deaf, instead of the priest, "We take care of each other." Sometimes she'd take Ralph's arm as they walked down the church steps and he would bend his elbow the way he'd seen a man do on television. She'd smile up at him and say in a sweet voice, "How about you take me to the WagonWheel for pancakes, son?"

On those Sundays Ralph thought his heart felt large, and full. At other times his mother's voice scraped at him like a sharp tool. It grilled him when he arrived home a few minutes late: "You stopped to talk to *who*? How long could that *take*?" This voice made his palms itch. He'd vow to be careful next time Marcella Cooper stopped to talk in the parking lot after work. He'd remember to tell Tim, the butcher at Freeman's, that he couldn't "shoot the breeze" about the Cowboys' game.

But the surge of happiness Ralph felt when anyone paid him attention made him forget, again and again. When he was late, his mother would have a second and even a third drink before dinner, which made her voice more harsh and his palms more itchy.

Thirty years later, Ralph was still forgetful and often late. His mother was now almost eighty, but her voice had lost none of its sharpness. One fall night in 2003, he wasn't late. He didn't take too long to park the van, no one approached him to chat, and he walked the three blocks home at a fast pace. He was exactly on time, he saw, glancing at the wristwatch his mother insisted he wear. When he turned the key in the front door, he expected her to call from the living room where she watched the evening news, "Miracle of miracles, he's on time!" Then, "Put your keys in the basket where they belong." The absence of her voice as he pushed open the heavy oak door was a tiny warning, so subtle he missed it.

He called, "Mother?" and tossed his keys at the basket in the front hall. The keys missed the basket and clattered on the floor. He scooped them up and put them in his pocket. The cold October air that entered with him was quickly lost in the dry heat of the house. His footsteps down the hall were uneven; his gait was still awkward at fifty-two. His arms, which seemed too long for his body, went rigid at his sides as he entered the living room.

She was in her usual place on the couch, her drink on the table beside her, but instead of reminding him to go to the back porch and take off his work shoes, his mother simply sat, her head slumped to her chest so that he couldn't see her face. Her legs were splayed in a way that almost made him laugh.

He stopped himself, understanding slowly that something was wrong. His mother often fell asleep on the couch after she'd drunk the second cocktail, the one he sometimes mixed for her once he'd changed out of his work clothes. But this was different. Her glasses had slid so far down her nose they seemed about to fall into her lap. And there was a bad smell.

Shit, he thought, reminding himself even as he thought it, that she hated the word. The smell grew, seemed to grasp at him. He covered his nose and backed slowly out of the living room, knocking askew a framed studio photograph of himself and his mother taken last year. For a moment he waited to hear her voice, "Clumsy, Ralphy!"

But she said nothing. He kept moving backwards until he stood beside the kitchen doorway. Late-day sunlight filtered through the leaves on the willow tree into the kitchen. Ralph stared at the light, understanding that as soon as the wind tore the last of these leaves away, winter would move in to stay. Right now the sun seemed a golden gift, and Ralph felt an openness, something he didn't remember ever feeling before, as he stood still, watching the shifting shadows. He felt breath rising in his belly, softening, rising again. He could stand here as long as he wanted. Forever, maybe.

After a few minutes, a stab of dread broke through this peace. He walked slowly toward the phone, punched in the numbers his mother had helped him memorize. He got confused for a moment, thinking *9-1-1, nine-eleven,* closing his eyes against the image of planes plunging through buildings. "Emergency. 502 West Willow Street. Mother is quiet," he heard himself say.

"Ralph?" the dispatcher said. "It's Lee Halsey here." Lee attended the same Sunday mass as Ralph and his mother, and his voice was kind. "Your mother—is she breathing?" Ralph hated to admit he didn't know, so he said nothing. A minute ticked by, then Lee's voice again, "It's okay, Ralph. We're on the way. Is Angie Morton home next door?"

He put down the receiver; he could already hear the siren coming down Pine Street. He turned on the cold faucet, cupped his hands under the stream of water, then sucked at it.

Were voices coming from the living room? "News on the television," he said aloud. There was no voice telling him to turn off the TV, to get a glass if he wanted water, to change his work clothes and wash his hands. Even with the TV voices from the living room—a commentator saying there weren't enough American troops in Iraq and a deeper voice arguing—Ralph felt a strange, immense quiet all around him.

Mrs. Morton invited him for dinner that night. She wanted him to stay overnight at her house, but he insisted he'd rather be at home. "Mother was old enough to die. I am old enough to stay alone."

Later, he crossed the concrete driveway between their houses. He was careful to lock the front door and hang the towel properly after he brushed his teeth. He turned out the hall light. He stood for a moment at the door to his mother's bedroom. His mother didn't like it when he closed his bedroom door at night. *What if I need you for something and you can't hear me?* He remembered how some nights she asked him to rub cream on her feet.

He closed the door to her room, entered his own, and shut the door. He stood for a moment, listening to the quiet. Before he went to sleep, he allowed himself to cry, soundlessly, lying on his back, his hands in tight fists, his eyes squeezed closed.

Mary arrived early the next morning. Her dark, curly hair stood up in puffs around her pale face. "You seem okay," she said to Ralph, who sat at the kitchen table, a plate with his toast and cereal in front of him, his glass of orange juice on a small cocktail napkin so that it wouldn't make a ring on the table. When she spoke, Mary widened her round, dark eyes, so different from Ralph's deep-set blues under his unruly gray brows.

"I can make breakfast," Ralph stated. "I thought I could, and it was… not… hard." He stood to face his older sister. "I could make your breakfast, too." She told him she'd already eaten, and smiled at him. He cocked his head, looking at her. "You look kind of like Mother, but you smile easier." Mary hugged him. He was surprised and anxious when tears rolled down her cheeks onto his shirt, leaving three damp spots on the fabric.

Don't cry, he wanted to say, *Mother will not like it,* but then he told himself for the hundredth time since his mother's body was taken to the mortuary the night before: *Mother died.*

Mary pressed her cheek against his chest, her hair soft under his chin. "It's been too long since I've come, I know," she said through her tears. Ralph stood awkwardly, his large hands at his sides, until she let go.

"The rosary and viewing will be tomorrow," she told him. "The funeral, Friday." She pointed to their mother's room. "Come help me. We need to find the dress she wanted to be buried in." Now Mary's face looked different to Ralph, with lines he'd not noticed before around her mouth and two long grooves between her eyebrows.

"I am going to drive the truck today," he told her. "From 10 to 4 every day I deliver the groceries."

Surprise and a fleeting smile moved the lines beside her mouth. She shook her head. "Not tomorrow, Ralph. Or Friday. They'll understand. They probably don't even expect you today."

"I like to go," he said. "It is my job."

Mary finally nodded. "I understand. You go to work today. I have lots to do here."

When Ralph got home that afternoon they stood together at their mother's closet and found the bright coral silk dress their mother had often worn to church. "Mother likes church," Ralph said, remembering the good Sundays. He touched the dress gingerly, not wanting to wrinkle it. He blinked rapidly as Mary folded the dress and handed it to him, afraid he might cry again. My heart is aching, he thought, remembering the words of a song he'd heard on the radio.

That evening, he told Mary he would make their dinner while she rested on the couch. He put two TV dinners in the oven, but forgot to put the timer on, and they nearly burned. "That's the trouble with me. I always forget," he told Mary. "Like a little kid, Mother said."

"Everybody forgets stuff, Ralph," Mary answered. She found some green beans in the freezer and steamed them. She lit a candle, which Ralph knew his mother wouldn't like, but he enjoyed the way it made shadows on the kitchen walls. They ate the beans and picked at dry chicken cutlets and crusty mashed potatoes. Ralph felt the quiet again, even with Mary there. They left the light off, and sat for a while in the candlelight, their meals unfinished.

Mary sighed, then tucked a dark curl behind her ear. "Look, Ralph," she said, "I read Mother's will today in Don Smyth's office. You know, Mother's lawyer. She left everything in trust, with me as trustee. She wanted you to come live with me, or else…" Mary seemed to have trouble speaking; her voice became softer. "She wanted me to put you in the state home in Riverton."

"Whose home?" Ralph frowned, concentrating.

"The Home for the Retarded." Mary looked down at the table.

Ralph strained to figure out her words. Finally he spoke. "I am retarded. Mother said. Like a little kid. They only let me graduate because she made them. I already know that. Why do they call it home?" He rarely spoke so many sentences at one time; it made him breathless, and his heart beat faster. He put his hand flat against his chest.

Mary looked at him carefully. "It's just a way of talking, is all. But Ralph. I read the report from the doctor in Denver who tested you. Remember when you visited me in my first apartment? We ate in that cool restaurant the night before the tests? You were just out of high school."

"No," said Ralph. "I do not remember that." He remembered only the row of apartment doors that looked alike.

"Ralph," Mary said, "listen carefully to me."

"Wait," said Ralph. He flicked on the overhead light, ate the last two bites of his chicken, rinsed the tray under the tap, put it in the waste basket, sat, folded his napkin into squares, put it under his milk glass. "Okay," he said.

Mary was crying. She tried to speak, her voice catching between words. She took one of Ralph's hands in hers. "I-I don't know how to say this. I feel so…negligent, and…guilty." Ralph wanted to pull away from her touch, but he was fascinated by her crying, her voice, the tears, the messy wetness of her face and hands. He let his hand remain clasped in hers.

"Ralph, the test showed that you are a fully functioning person. You might not have a high I.Q. but you have enough skills—you had enough skills back then!—to live on your own. Mother just…"

Beads of sweat had appeared above Mary's lip and at her hairline. Ralph couldn't understand why she didn't wipe her face. He pulled his hand from hers and handed her his napkin. She stopped talking for a minute, blotted her face with the napkin, drew in breath. "Ralph. Jesus! In a bigger town the schools would have… Or if I'd taken more initiative myself, after Dad died…"

Ralph thought Mary seemed both angry and sad, which seemed too complicated. He wanted to run away from her, but she held him there, with her voice, which was rising. "It's all there, papers in Smyth's office. You had a fucking cleft lip. That's all that was really wrong! I didn't *get* it—until today." She pulled on his hand. "Mother convinced herself and everybody else that you were retarded, but you weren't—aren't!" Her words were tumbling out so fast now that Ralph had to stop listening. He knew somehow, but didn't want to know, the truth she spoke. Finally, she covered her face with her hands and was silent.

Ralph sat across from her without moving, until she finally sank back into her chair. Like a balloon with the air out, Ralph thought. Then he picked up her TV dinner tray from the table, scraped it off, and threw it in the wastebasket. He felt as if heavy weights were attached to his legs. He stood and patted her shoulder, afraid she'd fill up with air and begin swearing and crying again. "I need to sleep," he told her. She squeezed his hand, staring at the melting candle.

As soon as Ralph fell into bed, he was dreaming. He could see through Mary's clothes and skin, straight into her heart. It was a big heart, and it was full of doors and windows. The doors opened and slammed shut, the windows flew up, curtains blew out and were caught when the windows banged shut again.

The next day neighbors and church members began bringing food. All day, in and out, saying *so sudden* and *so sorry* and *poor Ralph, what will he do?* Mary nodded and was hugged, Ralph's hands were pumped and petted, Mary shoved casserole dishes into the fridge, Ralph carried plates and coffee mugs from the kitchen to the living room.

Then it was time to get ready for the viewing. Ralph put on the suit he wore to church and Mary tied his tie the way his mother had. "You could learn to do this for yourself," Mary said. "I'll teach you."

Ralph straightened his shoulders, looked in the mirror. His mother had sometimes said he was handsome in his suit, that he looked like his father. *You should have seen him, Ralphy, in his army uniform. Oh, he was a handsome man.*

Mary drove to the mortuary. On the way Ralph's foot began to itch. He stuck his finger down into the back of his sock, but couldn't reach the spot, so he took off his shoe and sock and scratched hard at the sole of his foot. When they parked, Mary turned off the motor, then smiled at him as he opened the car door.

"Maybe you should put your shoe back on," she said. They looked straight into each other's eyes for a moment, and Ralph almost smiled back, but he suddenly felt shy, and busied himself with his shoe.

Inside, he could see the casket from the back door of the carpeted room. There were candles on big brass candlesticks on either side. Both parish priests were there, greeting visitors. A scent of flowers and candle wax hung in the air. Mary took his arm and together they walked toward the casket.

Ralph put one hand over his chest, pressed his palm against a hammering. He could feel his neck and face turn red. He was afraid to look at his mother but could sense her face there, below the padded white silk of the raised lid. Mary grasped his hand harder. The priests were silent, watching them. Mary's grip kept him still, contained against the hammering. Slowly he made himself look down at his mother.

Her mouth was closed tight. Her thin lips were pressed closed, painted a soft color that matched the dress rather than her usual bright red lipstick.

Ralph drew breath into his lungs and felt Mary beside him, tense, her shoulders slightly hunched. His mother's closed eyes behind the plastic frames of her glasses would not open, ever. Whatever he did, his mother would not see, she would not speak. He felt both relief and an aloneness that was entirely new to him.

While the prayers of the rosary were recited—the priest leading and the handful of mourners muttering responses—Ralph stole a look at Mary. Her face was pale and the lines around her mouth deep. Ralph knew that after the rosary, and tomorrow at the funeral, every mourner would ask the same question: *What will you do with Ralph?* He was smart enough to know this would be harder for Mary than for him. She was the one they'd expect to answer.

That night Mary dug through the fridge, lifting the foil covers to peek at the various casseroles. "There must be something green in here somewhere," she said. Ralph reached above her head and pulled out the molded Jell-O salad from Mrs. Morton. Mary squinted at it and laughed "It's green all right, and I think there are apples in it. Barely discernible apples. I can't believe people still eat this stuff," she muttered as Ralph put the dish on the table.

"We'll serve all this food tomorrow, after the burial," she said, closing the door of the fridge.

"We have to make a lot of coffee for people," he said. "And highballs."

"Nobody says highball anymore, Ralph." Mary sat, put her elbows on the table, her chin resting on one hand. She looked exhausted.

"I could make you a highball right now," Ralph said, opening the cupboard where the Jim Beam sat. He measured three fingers of bourbon, one of soda, then dropped an ice cube into the glass. He handed it to Mary. "This is how mother taught me."

"You aren't having one?"

He looked at her, confused, and shook his head.

"Didn't you ever join mother at the cocktail hour?"

He shook his head again.

"Come on. Have a goddamn highball with me."

"I am too dumb to drink highballs," he said, but he took a second glass down and carefully measured out the whiskey, added the soda.

"Who says? Let's find out. Drink up." She clinked her glass against his.

He sipped at his drink. Mary finished hers, then brought the bottle to the table. She poured more whiskey into her glass and scooped up some Jell-O. "Jim Beam and Jell-O—only in River Springs." She ate a few more spoonfuls, watching Ralph closely as he sipped and grimaced at the taste of the whiskey.

"You were always so good," she said. "You never did anything at all rebellious—bad—did you?"

He had to think for a long time. He took a spoonful of Jello while he thought. His mother would not like the way they were eating right out of the dish. He enjoyed the way the Jell-O slid down his throat, without the effort of chewing.

"I was bad when I said shit-ass at dinner."

Mary dropped her spoon into the dish. "Oh my God, I remember! It was before your teeth were fixed, and you couldn't say it right. Mother was so upset. Remember?"

Ralph nodded. "Dad laughed."

Mary poured another two fingers of whiskey into her glass. "He laughed so hard he nearly fell off his chair." She stared out the kitchen window for a minute, then drained her glass and looked at Ralph. "My God, Ralph. It was cruel. No wonder you were always good. All that…judgment, from both of them. It makes me…" She looked away.

Ralph looked out the window at the tree. In a few minutes it would be dark. The chill in the kitchen meant winter was creeping closer. It was only October and he thought he could already feel the tree's branches grow cold. Soon they would be covered with snow. It would be Halloween and then Christmas and long months of shoveling the front walk, scraping ice off the delivery truck in the mornings, his teeth aching with cold on the walk home from work.

He was sorry he'd brought up that dinner. He felt confused by what the memory was stirring in him. His father laughing. The word *hyena*. The drink made his thoughts race, made him feel smart, then stupid, stirred up an unfamiliar mixture of hope and anger in his chest.

He waited for Mary to say something. He could see she was getting drunk, but in a different way than his mother after three highballs. Mary was frowning hard, as if it was difficult to concentrate, eating the green Jell-O, washing it down with his mother's whiskey. Ralph poured a little more into his own glass and drank. Maybe he'd get smarter with more.

"Ralph, what are we going to do with you?" Mary blurted suddenly. "I can't take you back with me. I can't stay here, and I sure as hell can't put you in Riverton. What do you *want* to do?"

Again he had to think hard, for long minutes. Slowly he stood up, carefully pushed his chair into the table, stretched to his full height and squared his shoulders. "I want to join the army and fight the terrorists in Iraq." He thought this sounded informed, like someone on TV.

Mary sprang to her feet. Her chair clattered to the linoleum floor. "What?! *That* is the *only* retarded thing I've ever heard you say!"

He was used to this kind of outburst. From Mary, it didn't seem frightening. She already looked sorry, standing there. He set her chair back on its legs and waited until she sat back down on it. He knew already that what he'd said was stupid.

He tried again. "I want to be like Dad—get a medal, and laugh," he said, sitting back down beside her.

"What do you mean, get a medal?" She looked like she might cry again.

"Dad's medal that looked handsome on his jacket. Wait." He went quickly to his mother's bedroom and brought back the picture of their father in his World War II uniform.

"Oh," said Mary, "I saw that medal today in the strongbox. It's a star."

"I want to change into a man like Dad in this picture," Ralph said, holding up the photo.

She shook her head. "You can't change in this town, Ralph. Nobody will let you. That's why I left."

He frowned deeply, concentrating with all his being on what she'd said. He closed his eyes, and breathed the way he had the night his mother died, when he'd looked out the window and felt the quiet. He thought about the tree outside the window. About how it lost its leaves and then grew them back again every spring.

Slowly, it came to him. He opened his eyes and cleared his throat. "I can do what you said nobody will let you," he said finally. "I can change in this town. I'm smart enough for that."

Mary blinked several times, her eyes wide. Black mascara had smudged under her eyes, and a piece of apple from the Jell-O was stuck in the corner of her mouth. "I'm sorry I yelled at you," she said, touching his hand. "I'm sorry about everything."

"It's okay," he said. "I don't mind." His heart felt too large for his chest.

"Do you realize…that you never laugh, Ralph? Why is that?"

He shrugged. "I do not laugh and I do not cry."

She laughed, a tired sound, and shook her head. "I do it for both of us, right?"

The day after their mother's funeral, Mary took their father's medal from the strongbox and gave it to Ralph. He pressed it to his chest, his palm learning the feel of the stiff ribbon and the star shape under it. He held it in place over his heart.

Mary stared intently at him. "You can stay here, Ralph. I talked the whole thing through with Smyth today, and we worked out a plan. The trust will pay Mrs. Morton to help with laundry and shopping, and whatever else you need. I'll come every month or so, but…Ralph, are you sure you can handle this?" She was looking at the awkward way he was attempting to pin the medal above the pocket of his delivery uniform shirt, under the *Freeman's* logo. "You'll be so…alone. You'll have to decide so many things for yourself." She faltered a minute. "Like…maybe you shouldn't wear the medal on your uniform every day. Keep it someplace special." She bit her lip.

Ralph couldn't answer; he had fixed the pin on his shirt and was now looking out the kitchen window, noticing that during the night the wind had taken the rest of the leaves from the tree. The empty branches made him sad. He knew in his bones how dark the house would be when he came home each afternoon, how the wind would moan at the windows all night long. He was sorry again for the dumb thing he'd said about joining the army. He was scared of living in the same old house alone, he was afraid of winter—how could he go fight terrorists?

He touched the medal, felt its hard points under his fingers. He knew he'd wear it every day, no matter what Mary said. It would be a reminder over his heart. With the medal in place, maybe he could change. He had never in his life done anything very difficult. His mother had made everything easy. He turned from the window and faced Mary. He would have to think now, think hard, about everything. ❧

The Way Back

Helen Klein Ross

After illness or raising children
The stunned body remains for a time

In stasis, contrarian
As the wasp at an opened window,

Clinging to peels of paint
On the sill. What sound

The brain makes, reeling
With what is left,

Left to be done. Starting
Out in the evening

I forge, a slow pilgrim, my way
Lit by moonflowers, white

Ash, the string of milk-teeth
Around my neck.

ଚ୦

The Storm Between Us

Hazel Kight Witham

I travel to Galveston to know my grandmother. I drive along the southeastern jaw of Texas, passing through towns named Cheek and Winnie until I veer onto the road that will take me to the Gulf. I stare out the window at the green land under a gray morning until the horizon disappears and I steer into the past.

My grandmother died six years before I was born. She never knew it, but she left me her old-fashioned name—Hazel—and an old-fashioned rose-cut diamond that became my engagement ring. She also left me an unfortunate sliver of DNA that has me traveling this two-lane road to Galveston.

Green marshland swims in the foreground. Silver slips of water roll away from the road and fade into a blur of mist. Oil derricks emerge, bowing their heads to the earth like horses wetting their lips at the trough. A line I cannot define is somewhere in the distance and I feel her gathering within me.

Galveston is an island tucked into a natural harbor along the Gulf of Mexico. At the turn of the twentieth century it was a bustling, prosperous port. It was the largest city in the state, full of Victorian mansions and long-limbed trees, beautiful beaches and people getting rich. No one expected the Storm.

Early on September 8, 1900, a Texas-sized hurricane pummeled the island. Flood waters surged over the banks, destroying nearly 4,000 buildings. More than 8,000 people died, crushed by debris and water. One in every five, gone. Countless unidentified bodies were cremated for public safety. Whole families died, making it difficult to track casualties. The dead took the details with them.

I search for details of my grandmother like gathering sea glass along a rocky beach—bright shards of stories I coaxed from my mother when I was young and we were driving at night, when the dark helped her remember.

Grandmother was born in Corsicana, Texas, and settled down 300 miles south in Orange with her high-school sweetheart, Robert. They had two daughters, eight years apart.

A story I love: when they moved into the Orange house, the movers put the piano on the front porch and my grandmother played tune after tune as the men lugged all their belongings into the home. Every time they asked her where something should go, she said, "Just put it on the back porch," and continued playing. As the afternoon wore on, one of the movers finally said, "Lady, have you taken a look at the back porch lately?"

My grandmother started deteriorating with the move away from Corsicana. She didn't know anyone in Orange; she didn't have a job or any real hobbies other than piano. As her world withered in that unfamiliar town, depression colored her daily life. When she gave birth to my mother, melancholy overwhelmed her nearly to the point of catatonia, and she was hospitalized in the Galveston Psychopathic Hospital.

The few things that remain in our family offer a glimpse of her. I know my grandmother had a brass chain-link purse that pooled in my hands like water. I know she had a fancy silver compact inlaid with lavender flowers. I know she hated photographs of herself. I know she didn't drive. I know she hated Galveston.

After the storm, Galveston took action with an intensity to match the hurricane. Residents cleaned up the wreckage, constructed a 17-foot seawall six miles along the Gulf coast, and pumped sand in from the sea floor to raise the island's grade.

But when another storm struck in 1915, the island was flooded again, killing as many as 400. In 1933, eleven storms pounded the coast of Texas. After each hurricane, Galveston had to reset itself.

For my grandmother, Galveston was always a place of storms. In the 1940s, the Psychopathic Hospital was one of the few of its kind in Texas. Over the course of five weeks, my grandmother underwent a series of electroconvulsive treatments, that she might be stunned out of her depression. ECT induces seizures, resulting in convulsions and a loss of consciousness. It was hoped that her brain would reset.

Like the cyclical nature of Galveston's hurricanes, my grandmother's moods stormed through her and periodically wreaked havoc on her life. Without much of interest to fill her days, her drinking increased. She stayed in bed more, glasses of Canadian Club sweating on the nightstand. She cried and grew restless. She would beg Grandpa not to take her back to Galveston, and at first he would acquiesce. But she would drift away in her bed, paralyzed, until she was surrounded by salt water and skies that held no light. She felt utterly hopeless, but she knew she didn't want shock treatments. He had to take her against whatever will she had left.

After her ECT, my grandmother would misplace the names of her daughters. The memory of her newborn child fogged over. Both her depression and its treatment seemed to inhibit her ability to care for the children. Her ability to play the piano, to do her hair, to keep house.

I would ask my mother about the hospital and the shock treatments, long before I knew that I had inherited my grandmother's illness. Every time there were new details and the same sadness. But so much was elusive and I needed something tangible. Something more than story to cast a light on what linked us.

So now I am going back. Along the same route, past fences her eyes must have tripped over, grasses the same green. I hit High Island and then Gilchrist. Suddenly all the houses along the shoreline seem as surprised as I am by the appearance of the ocean. They fear the worst, sitting high on stilts, lifting their skirts to show skinny legs where water can flow past and leave structures intact.

I wonder how deep the beams go, how firmly the foundations hold in a storm, what houses look like hovering on hurricane water. Which houses were here when Grandmother traveled this road? What did she understand of them when they returned from the hospital, her mind as fogged as this forgotten landscape? Nothing looks alive, despite the abundant green. The houses seem uninhabited. Vaulted in defiance of nature, shocked, and left in eternal awkwardness.

From the upper deck of a ferry I watch Galveston spread before me. Texas seagulls with black heads ride the wind off the bow of the boat all the way to the landing. I drive off the ferry and twist along the eastern edge of the 30-mile island. The old Psychopathic Hospital appears before I am ready: a great lawn opening up to a campus of tall buildings, pale brick, darkened glass. It is less than a mile from the ferry landing. She would have had so little time after getting off the boat.

The campus is larger now, I'm sure, with more buildings, but I bet that wide lawn was there on her first visit. She would have ridden by it on the looping drive toward the hospital. It could have been her last sight of grass for months. As the car nears the drive my body tenses and I cannot bring myself to turn toward the hospital. I've come so many miles to see this place and now I am flooded with the fear, the bone-deep dread of what awaited my grandmother here in Galveston. All I can think is how she wanted to be free of it and I cannot take us back. I hold my breath as I drive past.

My mother told me that once, after my grandfather had taken my grandmother to the hospital for treatment, she escaped the very next day. She walked to a local bar and convinced a stranger to take her on the ferry and drive her ninety miles back to Orange. And then my grandfather drove her right back again.

I marvel at how brave she was. Winding through the streets away from the hospital I wonder where the bar was, and did she get a drink before she headed back? She must have; my grandparents liked their liquor. I see her push past the swinging doors of my mind's Western saloon, backlit by the dust swirls of noonday light. A handful of people propped on stools nursing hangovers. Worn cowboy boots and trusty Stetsons. Hazel steadies her hand on the cool wood of the bar and orders a beer. Pinches some salt into the foam like her husband always does. This calms her.

How many people did she have to ask before some man agreed to drive her home, with the promise of money from her husband? Did she stand out or fit in perfectly? What was she wearing? Did they have those plastic hospital bracelets back then? And remembering my own hospitalization, what I want to know most: how did she manage to sneak out?

Thirteen years ago I fell into a depression during my first year in college. Unlike my grandmother, I had the benefit of medications for this illness I inherited. They worked and things got better, until the other side of our illness surfaced. The depression lifted and I promptly whirled into a mania that landed me in a psychiatric hospital for eight weeks. While I was there, thoughts of my grandmother came to me as I began to experience what for so long I had only imagined.

Passing Grandmother's hospital site I am back at my own, and the distance of thirteen years vanishes:

I walked the halls in stale scrubs, barefoot, scrounging cigarettes from other patients and staff. It became normal, acceptable, to pick up half-smoked cigarettes from the ground and massage them straight so they could fit into the safety lighter on the courtyard wall. As I smoked, I stared up at the strips of blue sky visible through the iron bars that secured the top of the cinder-blocked patio. Cigarettes were one of the few pleasures within that cage.

My meals were on trays; I slept in a single room on a metal bed. Doctors and nurses wrote notes on charts, trying out diagnoses to find one that would fit. They drew vials upon vials of blood, sticking the awkward inside of my elbow almost daily. Twice a day there were little paper cups cluttered with pink pills, blue pills, white pills.

There was nothing to do but climb around in the jungle of my restless mind. No art, no books, no music.

I took showers as often as I could, water falling like freedom for a few moments. I took too many apparently, because that became one measure of my sickness. One answer to my constant question: When can I leave? When I take fewer showers. When I stop going in other people's rooms. When I stop taking off my booties and walking around barefoot.

New conditions were invented at every turn, while a kaleidoscope of medications shifted my world from manic to catatonic, garrulous to thick-tongued, animated to anesthetized. I could refuse the horse tranquilizers, the anti-psychotics, but then I would be "resisting treatment" and that would only slow my release.

Days ticked by in a vacuum and I saw my life narrow down to nothing. I became convinced I would never leave.

Late one night, itching for freedom, I slipped out of my room. A horizonless exile compelled me to move. I flew down the long corridor, past the good sleeping patients, and aimed for the window at the end of the hall. I slammed into unyielding glass, pressed my head into the cold of it, whispering pleas to the night grass glowing in pools of lamplight.

Moments later, I was captured, like a wild mustang, and carried bucking back down the hall. It was a whirling chaos of movement—arms, legs, wrists, thighs, gripped tight and too close. I didn't know where I ended and they began. I fought with everything in me, but they knew what they were doing. They opened the door to my room and pressed me face down on my bed, one at each limb. A figure darkened the doorway, armed with a tangle of leather straps, all silver buckles and precise holes. My grandmother filled my mind, and we fought together, terrified of what was to come.

They strapped me down and I watched myself from above, an X across the bed, like I'd been shot in the back. A nurse plunged a needle into my hip and my sobbing faded and I stopped fighting.

When I came to, the sheets were soaked, the room dark. I began the glacial process of undoing the restraints. It was a test: if I could pass it—if I could get out—they would let me go. They would know I was not really crazy. They would not shock me.

I wrenched my right arm around, working one wrist out, straining for the next. I leaned back, knees twisting, to unbuckle the right ankle then the left. I was almost free when the faint stream of light entering the room wavered and I saw a head blacken the window in the door.

They did not want me free.

During the seven days they had me strapped to the bed, the few facts I knew of my grandmother stormed through me like so much lightning, so much wind. I knew her in a way I never had: the rage, the fear, the certainty that they would shock me as they did her.

Years after my hospitalization, I read about ECT, tried to understand what it must have been like. As I drive through Galveston now, one patient's comment echoes through my head: "Each shock treatment was for me a Hiroshima."

Those words confirm my worst fears.

Shock treatments back then, with their high voltages, were brain damage masked as therapy. Amnesia the goal, a deliberate fogging of the mind.

Experts now say that shock treatments are better, underutilized even. Voltages are milder, anesthesia is given. Psychiatrists tell of success stories; patients attest to its miraculous effects. Shock is not used to subdue or punish like it was in the asylums of long ago. The asylums of my imagination.

Part of me believes the experts, these cured patients.

But there remains in me an unquantifiable terror at having a body charged with so much electricity. Such a storm, so unstoppable, capable of losses that cannot be told. Part of me believes it was a Hiroshima.

Galveston has always sounded ominous to me. It was a long time before I realized that beneath its name another word lurks—galvanize:
1. to stimulate somebody or something into great activity
2. to coat a metal, usually iron or steel, with zinc to prevent corrosion
3. to stimulate the nerves or muscles of somebody's body using an electric current

One of the most difficult things about the hospital is after the hospital, when the self you are now searches for the self you were then. People don't treat you the same because they no longer know who you are. You have gone somewhere they don't want to imagine, and a new distance springs up between you.

When I returned home there was the wreckage of a former self to sort through, and I am sure this is how it was for my grandmother, hospitalized at a time when such things were even more taboo. Her friends tiptoed around her when they stopped by to visit, talked about the safe details of their lives while steering away from the gaping hole that had emerged in hers. She told some more than others, but the shame of being shocked must have been overwhelming. How could she let anyone know the truth of it? How could I tell anyone that they tied me up for seven days?

I know my grandmother's moments of darkness. Those moments are the same for everyone gripped by depression and utterly isolating when the dark closes in. All those days at home in bed, twisted in stale sheets—she sipping alcohol, me snubbing out cigarettes in overflowing ashtrays. So many days of hiding, avoiding a world that moved too fast for our molasses minds. Time stretched out before us like a Texas road in a Texas desert, and there was no horizon.

Though I never experienced shock treatments, I know that feeling of being at someone else's mercy. I know the rage and humiliation of having no say in your fate. Every time I ask my mother to tell Grandmother's story, I am always hoping for a different ending.

I drive along the sandblasted strip above the seawall, leaving the Psychopathic Hospital behind. The ward my grandmother stayed in is a ghost now, swallowed by modern buildings and medical advances. But I now know the drive she took, the scenery she tried to get lost in as she headed toward something that offered wellness through obliteration. Knowing that landscape brings me closer than the actual hospital would. I know her confinement; it is her glimpse of freedom that compels me.

I stare at my grandmother's diamond on my finger. This stone of love and hope is what keeps her with me now. Sometimes in my everyday life, when I'm driving in the late afternoon, thinking of nothing, light will stream in through the windshield and tangle with the facets, spraying the dashboard with dancing points of the past. It is a pattern she knew, in the passenger seat of Grandpa's Dodge, back when driving around with a new husband was fun.

And later, in the years that grew dim, perhaps she saw that sparkle when the sun streamed in through the window on the drive to Galveston. Before her flashed a constellation of diamond light, snapping her to the present, when a sunbeam dipped into a clear stone and painted the world new. Maybe for a moment she would forget what was to come.

I drive out of Galveston into a clear afternoon. There is blue in the sky, a line on the horizon I can hold onto. The details of this day illuminate a woman

I never met. Her blood courses through me, while the knowledge of her experience remains sharp as warning, a dark sky in the distance.

But now, against the blur of green that I pass—that she passed—if I move my hand just so, the new day will catch her diamond and send light dancing between us. ✤

Black Dog

Amie Sharp

> *When he comes the first thing he does is to worry my*
> *master. This time he gnawed him to the bone.*
>
> - Samuel Johnson, letter to Mrs. Hester Thrale

There's nothing I love so much
as that soft whine when my cage door

swings back. Smell that fresh air—
I can't wait to make it rancid.

You let me out, didn't you? So don't
ignore my scratches at your door.

Running away? Go ahead—tracking
your little hiding place is half the fun.

I'm not weak anymore. You stopped
starving me months ago. I've been waiting

to show you my new trick: I bare
my teeth and an abyss opens

right under your feet. Fall in,
listen to silence, except for my snarls.

These red veins streak across
my yellow eyes, my hackles rise,

and you just pull the covers tighter
over your face. So go on—bow

your heavy head again. Your sleep
is tastier than a rawhide bone.

And if you're lucky, you won't
even see what happens next.

&

Book Review

Right of Thirst

Frank Huyler

(New York: Harper Perennial, 2009, 384 pgs.)

Reviewed by Walter Cummins

In an interview supplementing this edition of his novel *Right of Thirst*, Frank Huyler, an emergency room physician, notes that although medicine has been "among the most repressed of all professions," the profession is changing and "more doctors [are] writing now than ever before." He divides these doctor-authors into two categories— those who write "elegant, well-crafted" essays about medical subjects and those who are writers as much as they are doctors. Huyler himself belongs to the second category. He is an essayist, a poet, and a very talented novelist.

In *Right of Thirst*, his first-person protagonist, Charles Anderson, happens to be a doctor, a cardiologist who teaches in a Michigan medical school. While medicine does have a role in the novel, his profession comes to matter little in Anderson's dilemma as a man facing a life crisis in late middle age; it could have been any high-status career that no longer satisfies his soul.

Far from home in the frigid mountains of an unnamed country much like Pakistan, Anderson finds himself performing life-saving surgery to amputate the pus-filled foot of a child, a girl named Homa from a local village. Huyler describes this tense procedure very effectively: "the rasp of [a saw] in my hands, the silver bar of the blade up and down, bloody and glistening from the bone ends." A novelist, however, does not need a medical degree to write such a scene. Consider Gustav Flaubert's description of Charles Bovary's grotesquely botched operation on a club foot. Anderson's surgery, in fortunate contrast, is successful. But other than a lesson in drawing blood, that is the only time his profession matters in the novel.

The story setup of *Right of Thirst* is familiar: a man burnt out after "decades of blind relentless work" seeks "something clear and redeeming." The novel opens with a scene of Anderson assisting his wife's death to free her from terminal suffering. Stunned by what has happened, estranged from his teaching duties, Anderson attends a lecture by a young man named Scott Coles, who seeks financial and human assistance for camps his new organization is creating to help earthquake victims. A doctor would be crucial, and Anderson signs on: "I suppose another world was what I wanted most." Once there, he hopes to finally make a difference for the first time in his life.

The familiar fictional pattern, of course, would be to have Anderson overcome some initial dislocation but soon minister to the sick and wounded, popping in and out of refugee tents to share his medical skills, and emerge a renewed and fulfilled man. Huyler is much more original; nothing like that happens. The refugees never arrive. Anderson's medical skills—beyond saving Homa—are never called upon. Although he faces severe physical, emotional, and moral tests, he must confront them at the most basic human level. His title, doctor, means nothing in the world he must endure.

Huyler's greatest strength is his crystalline prose, the evocation of places, people, and events in sentences that are, at the same time, precise and lyrical. The writing immerses the reader in the vividness of Anderson's world—the amputation, the shivering cold, the sickening food, the visit to a nearby village for blood samples, the inspection visit by a smug general, the aerial view of an idyllic lake, the days of arduous walking through icy mountain passes along a river route, an accidental drowning, the retrieval of the body. More than just incidents, these happenings develop the complexities of Anderson's relationships with the two other main characters—Captain Rai of the national army and Elise, the young German geneticist seduced into the project by Scott Coles and promised an opportunity to collect blood samples.

The novel's final section takes place in a crowded city totally unlike the empty mountains. Despite the many physical dangers of the journey that brought him here, it is in this city that Anderson's strength as a man is most tested. The journey has revealed to him his mistaken belief that his adventure was unique, his own, when it "was just the human story again." Yet in the city he makes decisive choices because "This trip has to mean something. Otherwise I can't go home." Once he is back in the United States, seeing his son waiting for him at the airport, he feels himself "go calm for the first time." His commitment to a cause turned out to be nothing like his expectation. Yet, although Anderson has not changed the world he entered, he has made a great difference for a few people and, as a result, for himself. That difference has nothing to do with his medical degree, but everything to do with his humanity.

Right of Thirst demonstrates Huyler's many gifts as a novelist—his ability to describe unusual settings with precise lucidity, to create complex characters, and to tell a compelling story. His richest gift, however, is the emotional power to make his readers care about the characters in this novel and be moved. ଛ

Walter Cummins has published more than 100 stories in literary journals, as well as memoirs, essays, and reviews. His story collections are *Witness, Where We Live,* and *Local Music.* For more than twenty years, he was editor of *The Literary Review.* He teaches in Fairleigh Dickinson University's MFA in Creative Writing program.

Contributors' Notes

Karina Borowicz has recent work in *American Letters and Commentary*, *Cream City Review*, and the *Southern Review*. Her translations have appeared in *AGNI Online* and *Poetry Daily*.

Jerry M. Burger is a professor of psychology at Santa Clara University. His short stories have appeared in *Potpourri*, *Wind Magazine*, *Karamu*, and *Lynx Eye*.

Regie Cabico is a spoken word pioneer and has won the Nuyorican Grand Slam. His work appears in *The Outlaw Bible of American Poetry*, *Bum Rush the Page: Def Poetry Jam*, and *My Diva: 65 Gay Men and the Women Who Inspire Them*. He has received literary fellowships from the New York Foundation for the Arts, the DC Commission for the Arts, and the 2006 Writers For Writers Award for his work with at-risk youth at Bellevue Hospital. He resides in Washington, DC.

Nancy Naomi Carlson is the prize-winning author of *Kings Highway*, *Complications of the Heart*, and *Imperfect Seal of Lips*. She is an associate editor for Tupelo Press and an instructor at the Bethesda Writer's Center. Her work has appeared in such journals as *Agni*, *Crazyhorse*, *Denver Quarterly*, *Poetry*, *Prairie Schooner*, *Shenandoah*, and the *Southern Review*. She is the K-12 counselor specialist for the Montgomery County Public Schools in Maryland.

P. Philip Cheung has been dividing his time since 1987 between his hometown of Toronto, Canada and various cities in China where he lives, writes, and teaches ESL. His father was a physician at the former Toronto Hospital for Tuberculosis for thirty years. His mother's side of the family now includes the fifth generation of Torontonians of Chinese descent. His writing has appeared in *Gaspereau Review*, *lichen*, and *Metropolis*.

Claudia Cortese is a recent graduate of Sarah Lawrence College's MFA program, where she was the poetry editor for *Lumina Magazine* and a featured graduate reader at the Sarah Lawrence Poetry Festival. Her work has appeared in *At-Large Magazine*. She teaches English at Montclair State University in New Jersey and lives in New York.

Magda Montiel Davis immigrated to the United States as a child, shortly after the Cuban Revolution. She is an immigration lawyer, a former Democratic nominee for U.S. Congress, and the author of the nonfiction manuscript *Kissing Fidel.* Somewhere along the line she had five children and four grandchildren. She lives in Miami, Florida with her husband, Ira Kurzban.

Kelly Flanigan teaches high school English, instructs yoga, and works part time at a funeral home. She writes short stories and poetry, focusing primarily on young adults and the end of life. She lives in Shakopee, Minnesota with her puppy, Gatsby. She was named as an Honorable Mention for Fiction in the 2006-2007 Loft Mentor Series in Minneapolis. This is her first print publication. Her blog is: stephenkingsgirl.blogspot.com

John Kay is a poet and photo-artist who lives in Heidelberg, Germany. He has an MFA from the University of Arizona, and previously taught writing at the University of Maryland in the European Division. He has three chapbooks and a forthcoming book, *Phantom of the Apple*, from Beginner's Mind Press. His photos can be viewed at www.pbase.com/jakay.

Amy Kitchell-Leighty holds an MFA in poetry from Bennington College's Writing Seminars. Her work has appeared in *Rockhurst Review*, *White Pelican Review*, and *All Things Girl.*

Anne Korkeakivi recently completed her first novel, *When Last I Saw You*, and is compiling a collection of short stories about displaced and misplaced persons. Some of these stories have appeared in the *French Literary Review* and the *Berkshire Review*. Her nonfiction has been published in the *New York Times*, the *Wall Street Journal*, and the *Times* (London). A native New Yorker, she currently lives in Switzerland.

Itzhak Kronzon has published over eighty short stories, both in his native Israel and in America. Three books—*Mother, Sunshine, Homeland*; *Who Will Get Belgium?* and *A Long Day's Journey into the Heart*—were published in Hebrew. He is a cardiologist and professor of medicine at NYU School of Medicine, as well as a senior professor at Tel Aviv University, and director and consultant at Escorts Heart Institute in New Delhi, India.

Jacqueline Jones LaMon is a graduate of Mount Holyoke College, UCLA School of Law, and Indiana University Bloomington, where she received her MFA in Poetry. A graduate fellow of Cave Canem, her first poetry collection, *Gravity, U.S.A.*, received the Quercus Review Press Poetry Series Book Award. Her first novel, *In the Arms of One Who Loves Me*, was published by One World/Ballantine Books. She is Director of Creative Writing at Adelphi University, where she teaches creative writing, literature, and pedagogy.

Patricia Lockwood's poems have appeared or are forthcoming in *American Letters & Commentary*, *Bat City Review*, *Chelsea*, *Cincinnati Review*, *Quarterly West*, the *Virginia Quarterly Review*, and *Witness*. She lives in Florida.

Matt Lombardi received an MFA from The New School. His work has appeared in *Details*, *Court Green,* and *Forklift Ohio*. He teaches English at Baruch College and lives in Brooklyn, New York. He is currently finishing his first novel.

Flavian Mark Lupinetti is a cardiothoracic surgeon in southern Oregon and an MFA candidate at the Vermont College of Fine Arts. Among his recent and forthcoming publications are stories in *Barrelhouse*, *Cutthroat*, *New Fables*, *Yellow Medicine Review*, and *ZYZZYVA*, some of which can be read at www.lupinetti.com.

Luther Magnussen's fiction has appeared in the *Yale Review*, *Harvard Review*, the *Antioch Review*, and *Harper's* and is also forthcoming in the *Pushcart Prize Anthology XXXIV*. He lives in New York City.

Kurt Magsamen has a degree in English from Colorado State University and a degree in American Studies from Utah State University. Among other jobs, he has worked as a craps dealer, hazardous materials laborer, and geographic-information-systems technician. He currently teaches English at the University of Pavol Jozef Šafárik in Košice, Slovakia.

MaryLee McNeal writes fiction and poetry. "Smart Enough" is from her manuscript titled *Another Wyoming*. "Blown to Cheyenne," from that collection, won the 2004 Palo Alto Weekly Short Story competition, and "Winter Light" was nominated for a Pushcart Prize after publication in the *BLR*. McNeal lives near San Francisco, where she teaches with the California Poets in the Schools, and leads poetry workshops at Hope House, a drug and alcohol recovery program.

Sandra Meek is the author of three books of poems—*Biogeography*, winner of the Dorset Prize; *Burn*; and *Nomadic Foundations*—and editor of *Deep Travel: Contemporary American Poets Abroad*, winner of a 2008 Independent Publisher Book Award Gold Medal. She is Poetry Editor of the *Phi Kappa Phi Forum*, Co-founding Editor of Ninebark Press, Director of the Georgia Poetry Circuit, and professor of English at Berry College.

Sequoia Nagamatsu was born in Ventura, California and grew up in Hawaii and Silicon Valley. He studied anthropology at Grinnell College, Iowa, and has produced stage performances in California and taught English in Japan. He is currently working on a novel and a story collection focusing on the Japanese Diaspora. His stories have appeared in *Elimae* and *One World: A Global Anthology of Short Stories*.

Joanna Pearson recently received her MFA in poetry from the Johns Hopkins University Writing Seminars, and she will complete her MD at the Johns Hopkins School of Medicine in 2010. She received Honorable Mention for the 2007 *BLR* prize in poetry. Her work has appeared in *Best New Poets 2005* and is forthcoming in *Gulf Coast, Tar River Poetry, Measure,* and *Valparaiso Poetry Review*.

Paola Peroni was educated at the University of Pennsylvania. Her stories have appeared in *Bellevue Literary Review*, the *Antioch Review, Alaska Quarterly Review,* and *Fence*. One of her stories was selected for the 2009 Prize issue of the *Mississippi Review*, edited by Frederick Barthelmy.

Patrick Pfister is the author of two books of travel literature: *Pilgrimage: Tales from the Open Road* and *Over Sand & Sea*. His work has been selected for several Travelers' Tales anthologies, including *Best Travel Writing 2007*. His stories and poetry have appeared in *Pearl, Fifth Wednesday Journal, Alimentum, International Quarterly,* and *Chiron Review*. He lives in Barcelona, Spain. www. patrickpfister.com

Ines P. Rivera Prosdocimi's work has appeared or is forthcoming in *Afro-Hispanic Review, Borderlands: Texas Poetry Review, Border Senses, Brush Mountain Review, Hispanic Cultural Review, PALABRA: A Magazine of Chicano & Latino Literary Art,* and *Revista LENGUA*. In 2008, she won first-runner-up in the *Pan African Literary Forum (PALF), Africana Poetry Contest*. Ms. Rivera just completed an MFA in Creative Writing at American University.

Helen Klein Ross is an advertising executive who lives in Manhattan. Her poetry and fiction can be found in *Salmagundi*, *Mid-American Review*, and *Quick Fiction*. Essays have appeared in the *New York Times*. She has received a Pushcart Prize nomination and is at work on a novel.

Christopher Schacht is a native Nebraskan who is currently pursuing an MFA in creative writing at New Mexico State. He graduated from Simpson College in Iowa with a BA in English and History, and briefly attended law school before escaping with his soul. "Shark Eyes" is his first published story.

Amie Sharp lives with her husband in Colorado Springs, where she teaches English at Pikes Peak Community College. A recent graduate of the Seattle Pacific University MFA program, her work has appeared in the *2River View* and the *New Formalist*.

Hal Sirowitz is the former Poet Laureate of Queens, New York. He has had Parkinson's for sixteen years and recently underwent a deep brain stimulation operation. He is the author of four collections of poetry. His first—*Mother Said*—was translated into nine languages. His most recent book is *Father Said*.

Melissa Stein's poems have appeared in *Southern Review*, *American Poetry Review*, *New England Review*, *Indiana Review*, *Gulf Coast*, and *North American Review*. Her work has won several awards, and she has received residency fellowships from Yaddo, MacDowell, Djerassi, Montalvo, Ragdale, and VCCA. She has an MA in poetry from the University of California at Davis, and is a freelance writer and editor in San Francisco.

David Wagoner has published eighteen books of poems, most recently *A Map of the Night*. One of his ten novels—*The Escape Artist*—was made into a movie by Francis Ford Coppola. He won the 1991 Lilly Prize and six prizes from *Poetry*. He was chancellor of the Academy of American Poets for twenty-three years. He has been nominated for the Pulitzer Prize and twice for the National Book Award. He edited *Poetry Northwest* until 2002. He is professor emeritus of English at the University of Washington.

Maria Williams-Russell received an MFA in poetry from Goddard College and a BA from Eugene Lang College of The New School. Her poems have been published in *Sous Rature*, *Chronogram*, and *Holly Rose Review*. She is the editor of the fine-arts website ArtId.com and teaches English Composition at Greenfield Community College. Maria lives in Greenfield, Massachusetts with her husband and two children.

Wendy Wisner's first book of poems, *Epicenter*, was published in 2004. Her poems have appeared in the *Spoon River Review*, *Natural Bridge*, *Flint Hills Review*, *RUNES*, and *5AM*. Wendy received an MFA in poetry from Hunter College, and her awards include the 2003 Amy Award. She lives in Bayside, New York with her husband and son.

Hazel Kight Witham is a writer, artist, and middle school teacher in Los Angeles, California. She has an MFA in Creative Writing from Antioch University-Los Angeles and is working on a novel and a memoir about her family's history with mental illness. www.hazelwitham.com

Acknowledgments

We are deeply grateful to all who have helped support the *Bellevue Literary Review* in its efforts to bridge the worlds of literature and medicine. Special thanks to the Goldenberg family, Marica and Jan Vilcek, and Gloria Vanderbilt and Anderson Cooper for their sponsorship of the *Bellevue Literary Review* Prizes.

 This publication is made possible with public funds from the New York State Council on the Arts, a state agency.

Founder: The Vilcek Foundation

Scribe: The Lucius N. Littauer Foundation

Publisher: Dr. Alec S. Goldenberg, Pfizer Inc.

Benefactors: Dr. Kay Redfield Jamison, Drs. Anthony & Elayne Mustalish, Rita J. & Stanley H. Kaplan Family Foundation, Billie Tisch

Muses: Dr. Michael S. Bruno, Dr. Joseph Dancis, H. Dale & Elizabeth Hemmerdinger, Lola Finkelstein, Dr. Katherine Mathews

Friends: Dr. Edward L. Amorosi, Dr. Jack Ansell, L.A. Bruell, Dr. Peter Elsbach, William Lee Frost, Dr. Charles S. Hirsch, Richard & Arlene Kossoff, Dr. Mark S. Lipton, Dr. Eric R. Marcus, Dr. Robert Maslansky, Dr. Richard Nachtigall, Eleanor Jackson Piel, Dr. Lionel Rudolph, Dr. William Schaffner, Drs. Sandy Zabar & Ira Breite

Supporters: Dr. Richard J. Baron, Dr. Charles H. Debrovner, Dr. Arthur C. Fox, Dr. Loren Wissner Greene, Dr. Martin L. Kahn, Dr. Franco Muggia, Dr. Diana Nilsen, Dr. Paul A. Tunick

----

We welcome your support as we continue to explore the connections between literature and medicine. All patrons will be recognized in the journal.

$75 (Supporter), $150 (Friend), and $250 (Muse) — *each includes one-year subscription for you and a friend*
$500 (Benefactor) and $1000 (Publisher) — *each includes three-year subscription for you and a friend*
$5000 (Scribe) and $10,000 (Founder) — *each includes lifetime subscription*

The *Bellevue Literary Review* is part of NYU Langone Medical Center, a 501(c)(3) charitable organization. All contributions are tax-deductible. Please make checks payable to NYU Langone Medical Center - *BLR*.

Bellevue Literary Review, Department of Medicine, NYU Langone Medical Center
550 First Avenue, OBV-A612, New York, NY 10016
www.BLReview.org